599.744   Rue

The world of the red fox
                    121059

D1214752

THE WORLD OF THE RED FOX

LIVING WORLD BOOKS

John K. Terres, Editor

The World of the Red Fox

Text and Photographs by
Leonard Lee Rue III

J. B. LIPPINCOTT COMPANY
Philadelphia and New York

Copyright © 1969 by Leonard Lee Rue III
All rights reserved
First Edition
Printed in the United States of America
Library of Congress Catalog Card Number: 69-16165

599.744

To my sister
Evelyn Rue Guthrie

121059

Contents

Author's Introduction

THE RED FOX is my favorite wild animal. Over a period of more than thirty years, I have spent thousands of hours in the field studying the fox, and I am still fascinated by everything I can learn about it. I make no apology for the fact that the basis for most of my knowledge of wildlife and its ways stems from what I learned as a trapper.

As a boy raised on a farm, trapping was one of the few sources of extra money available to me. I spent every minute that I could spare, winter or summer, in the woods, the fields, or on the river. The knowledge of wildlife that I gained all year long was put to use during the trapping season. And because of this knowledge, I was successful.

Foxes are the most intelligent fur bearers in my home state of New Jersey, and they provided a real challenge. It was a number of years before I could rightfully claim to be a fox trapper, but I improved until finally I was able to take ninety-three foxes in less than a six-week period, doing my trapping in addition to holding down a full-time job.

About that time a very good friend of mine, Art Wilkens, interested me in photography. As I became proficient with a camera, I realized that by the use of this medium I could actually "have my cake and eat it, too." I could work with wildlife, meeting their challenges without harming them, and from the photographs I could still realize a financial return. I started by selling photographs to illustrate other people's writings and then gradually began to write about wildlife on my own. At the same time, my wildlife lectures began to burgeon. After many

11

years of hard work, I was finally able to devote all my time to wildlife study, photography, lecturing, and writing. Whatever success I have attained today is based on the fundamentals of wildlife that I learned years ago as a trapper.

This book has been a labor of love in which I have tried to put down all the knowledge that I have about the red fox. A glance at the bibliography will prove that I realized my own shortcomings, and so I have tapped every source of material on the red fox that I could locate. My thanks to the authors listed there.

Many individuals have aided me over the years in gathering red fox material and in research. The one who has given me the greatest assistance is Joseph Taylor. Joe is more than just a good friend; he has always been an ideal to me. I think that Joe knows more about foxes than any other man and many foxes do. I can never thank him enough.

My thanks, too, to Fred Blayden, Ralph Bunn, G. E. Derrickson, Bud Disbrow, Russell Emele, Joseph Neff Ewing, Henry Fremont, L. F. Gingery, C. R. Grondahl, Arthur Halloran, William J. Hamilton, Jr., Charles O. Handley, Jr., Bill Hansen, Leon Kitchen, Levi Kries, Roger Latham, A. Mackay-Smith, Adolph Murie, John Paradiso, David Plank, Frank Sampson, Thomas G. Scott, Hilbert R. Siegler, Keith Sikes, Shirlee A. Smith, Fred Space, Nelson Swink, Jr., Charles and Ruth Traver, and Richard Van Gelder.

I also want to express my appreciation and special thanks to my sister, Evelyn Guthrie, for taking the time from her own very busy schedule to decipher my handwriting and to type this manuscript.

March, 1968   *Leonard Lee Rue III*

Meet the Red Fox

DOWN THROUGH the centuries the red fox has been celebrated in story and fable as the living symbol of intelligence. Such metaphors as "foxy," "sly as a fox," "crafty as a fox," "cunning as a fox" and such adjectives as wily, clever, audacious, and sagacious all acknowledge the high esteem that we, willingly or unwillingly, have for this animal.

Aesop has enshrined the fox in eleven of his famous Greek fables that have been told and retold over the past 2,500 years and has made the phrase "sour grapes" very much a part of our modern language. No one has attempted to date the fox legends that have been told by the Scandinavians, the Eskimos, the Siberians, the Chinese, and the Japanese. Olaus Magnus, a Swedish historian living from 1490 to 1558, wrote of the fox's getting rid of fleas by holding a stick in its mouth and slowly backing into water. The fleas were supposed to have passed up over the fox's body, to have congregated on the stick, and to have been set afloat as the fox escaped flealess. Variations of this story are still being told, but where did Magnus hear of it?

Geoffrey Chaucer paid tribute to the red fox around 600 years ago when he wrote:

> "A wily fox, that having spide,
> Where on a sunny bank the lambs doo play,
> Full closely creeping by the hinder side,
> Lyes in ambushment of his hoped prey."

The red fox lives up to its reputation for being a clever animal.

Meet the Red Fox

Joel Chandler Harris, in his Uncle Remus stories, had Br'er Rabbit outsmarting the fox at every turn. Thornton W. Burgess's Peter Rabbit was also able to escape from Reddy Fox, but Burgess kept his fox much more in character than did Harris. And so it is that through such tales, legends, and verse, all of us have been exposed to some information, true or false, about the fox.

The red fox is one of the most liked or disliked of all North American mammals, and that is just about the only fact about the fox on which most people might agree. Beyond that point, they call the fox by different names; in fact, some end up calling each other different names. It seems that the economic or aesthetic worth of the red fox can seldom be discussed with logic or without emotion because this animal either appeals, or does not appeal, to most people.

The chicken farmer considers the red fox an enemy; the orchardist calls him a friend. The small-game hunter, believing that the red fox is an "enemy" of rabbits and quail, would like to eliminate the fox; the trapper tries to take its fur; and the fox hunter would like to eliminate both the small-game hunter and the trapper. A naturalist may find it deeply satisfying to sit in a blind and study or photograph foxes, but officials in the conservation departments may be under pressure from hunters to control an eruption of the fox population. Any creature that feeds on another creature is classified as a predator, and the fox is a predator. Whether it is considered beneficial or not depends on "whose ox is being gored."

If I were asked for a one-sentence description of a red fox, I would sum it up as follows: A red fox is a sharp-featured, medium-size member of the dog family with reddish-yellow fur and a bushy tail, fleet of foot, and often showing more than average animal intelligence.

At the risk of being accused of anthropomorphizing, my long association with red foxes has led me to the conclusion that the red fox is capable of learning from new experiences—that its behavior does not always follow an instinctive pattern. Curiosity and the ability to learn are attributes of intelligence, and the red fox as a species is intelligent. I say as a species because just as some people are smarter than others, so some foxes are smarter than others. Many of the young red foxes do not display intelligence because of youthful inexperience, while some of the older foxes must be considered among the most canny in the animal world.

The Latin name for the North American red fox is *Vulpes* (meaning "fox") *fulva* (meaning "yellow") because, despite its common name, our red fox is not really red at all. The typical red fox's basic color may shade from a deep burnt rust to the palest golden yellow. The darkest basic color is down the center of the fox's back and behind the head, shading lighter toward the belly, which is a lead white. The tail is about the same color as the back but with black hairs interspersed. The terminal 3 to 4 inches of the tail is *always* white, making this a positive identification mark of the red fox. One red fox in New Jersey had an unusually long, 9-inch white tail tip, while others have just a few white hairs. The inside of the ears, the cheeks, the throat, and the chest are white. The nose, the back of the ears, and the lower part of all four legs are black. The eyes are bright yellow. The fox's whiskers are black and long and grow in five short rows.

The description I have just given would allow you to recognize a red fox but doesn't do it justice. To be fortunate enough to see the sun shining on a red fox as it stands against a pristine snowscape is to see the "beau ideal" of the animal world. Its coat, captured by the sun, takes on the tints and highlights of burnished gold and copper. The wind playing in its fur, as if passing through a summer wheatfield, causes a constant change in its shadings and hues. These are subtleties that the eye can capture but the pen cannot.

The red fox, however, also has several different distinct color phases. These are linked to cold weather or altitude, becoming common only in the northern portion of the fox's range, or on the higher mountains. In addition to the general reddish-yellow phase, this fox has colors that have given it the names of "cross fox" and "silver fox."

The term "cross fox" often conjures up a vision of a red fox that has been crossed or bred to a silver fox or to any member of the dog family, such as a wolf, a coyote, or a domestic dog. This is not true because the red fox apparently cannot produce young if it is bred to any member of the dog family that is not of its own genus. Ernest Thompson Seton mentions that a Lord Crandley in England bred a tame European male red fox to a black-and-tan terrier bitch, and the one resulting puppy had some of the color and external characteristics of each of the parents. Genetically, this is not possible. Wolves, coyotes, and dogs, however, can and do cross because they are of the same genus.

A fox is referred to as a cross fox not because of its breeding but because of a dark brown stripe of hair that extends from the fox's head

An Alaskan trapper displays a cross fox skin.

down the center of its back. This stripe is transected or crossed by another dark stripe behind the fox's withers. The cross fox's basic body color is a brownish-red.

The silver fox is a melanistic red fox and may appear as a black fox with the tips of the guard hairs tinged with silver. There are usually enough silver-tipped guard hairs to give the fox a beautiful frosted appearance. Or the fox's undercoat and guard hairs may be completely black. But no matter what the color phase, the red fox *always* has a white tail tip. I can find no record of an albino red fox in North America, although one was reported in the Asiatic red fox.

These color variations are merely genetic mutations and may or may not reproduce the same color phase in their own offspring.* All three color phases are often found in one litter. A. P. Low, in *Mammals of Labrador,* wrote of finding a den of red foxes that contained a litter consisting of two red pups, three cross pups, and two silver pups.

Figures compiled over a period of years from the Hudson Bay Company's records of their total fox take show that 5.1 per cent were silver foxes; 20.4 per cent, cross foxes; and the balance, normal red foxes. The silvers were most dominant in the North and Northwest, the cross in the center of the fox's range, and the reds in the southern part. In the past there have been localized places in the red fox's range where the silver fox predominated.

In 1774 the Russian Solovief, who commanded the ship *Sv Pavel,* returned to Okhotsk, Siberia, after four years on the Aleutian Islands and the Alaskan Peninsula. His cargo contained 1,900 sea otters, 1,493 black or silver foxes, 2,115 cross foxes, and 1,275 red foxes.

Because of its corresponding high value, the silver phase of this fox

---

*Editor's Note: The color variations in the red fox are apparently genetically determined. The genes for the normal, or reddish to yellowish, color of the red fox are usually dominant; the black "silver" fox, with the silver-tipped guard hairs, and the cross fox, with its dark brown stripe down the center of the back, appear less frequently in the red fox population because the genes for them are recessive to the normal color of the red fox over most of its range.

18

has been hunted and trapped so heavily that it is unlikely that even the Hudson Bay Company's percentages hold true today.

There is also a red fox that is referred to as a "Samson," "scorched," "burnt," or "bastard" fox. This is not a color phase but a skin condition in which the underfur is produced but no guard hairs. Such skins have

The arctic fox's fur turns white in winter.

no commercial value in the fur trade. The name "Samson" was applied to this condition because of the account in Judges 15:4–5:

"So Samson went and caught three hundred foxes, and took torches; and he turned them tail to tail, and put a torch between each pair of tails. And when he had set fire to the torches, he let the foxes go into the standing grain of the Philistines, and burned up the shocks and the standing grain, as well as the olive orchards."

Many inexperienced people confuse the red fox with the gray fox because the gray fox does have considerable rusty red along its face, neck, belly, and flanks. However, the gray fox has a *black* tail tip; the red fox *always* has a white tail tip.

The gray fox has a black mane on top of its tail.

Meet the Red Fox

An ever popular carnival booth is the one where a man guesses a contestant's weight and gives a prize if he is wrong. People are sure that they can win because they are quick to realize their inability to accurately estimate or guess the actual weight of anything and think the man in the booth will have similar failings. Scales have destroyed more good hunting and fishing stories than they have substantiated. Hunters see more red foxes than do most other people, and so it is the hunters' estimates of foxes' weights that get spread around. If the hunter shoots a fox and then carries it 2 miles back to his car, the fox gains weight not only with distance but later in the telling.

The red fox is actually small in size but appears larger in life. It weighs between 8 and 11 pounds with an average weight of about 9½ pounds, or about the weight of a large, well-fed housecat—though its long, silky fur makes it appear to be at least twice that weight. A fox that has been skinned displays a long, lean body built like a miniature greyhound. Running over the ground evolved its long, thin legs and the strong back muscles which are necessary to the fox's way of life. The chest is small and can easily be encircled by a man's hands.

A full-grown male fox measures 38 to 42 inches in length, of which the tail is 14 to 16 inches. It stands 14 to 16 inches high at the shoulder, and the ears are about 3½ to 4 inches long. The female is slightly smaller in size and lighter in weight.

The heaviest red fox of the hundreds that I have taken weighed 11¾ pounds. The heaviest red fox I ever weighed was given to me by my friend Joe Taylor in April, 1967. This large male weighed 14 pounds 12 ounces, stood 16 inches high at the shoulder, was 42 inches in total length, and had a chest girth of 15¾ inches. Its body was not any larger than that of other large red males; it was just that it was in excellent condition and weighed more.

Foxes in different regions of the country may be larger or smaller than the subspecies in others. Roger Hoffman and Charles M. Kirkpatrick, conducting fox studies in Tippecanoe County, Indiana, weighed fifty-two red males and fifty-two red females. The males weighed between 8.4 pounds and 13.4 pounds and averaged 11.57 pounds. The females ranged from 7.4 pounds to 12.5 pounds and averaged 9.28 pounds. These weights are considerably above the national averages. The females were heavier because many of them were pregnant. The weight of the stomach contents averaged 3.6 ounces. The capacity of a fox's stomach is about 16 ounces.

Walter Lasch of Conneaut Lake, Pennsylvania, while fox hunting on January 15, 1967, shot a red fox that weighed just a fraction over 16 pounds on commercial scales.

Ernest Thompson Seton recorded one male red fox raised on the fur farm of E. Norton at Dover, Maine, which weighed 16¾ pounds. Although I can find no weight greater than this, it must be remembered that on the fur farm the fox had unlimited food and, of even greater significance, limited exercise.

A red fox skull.

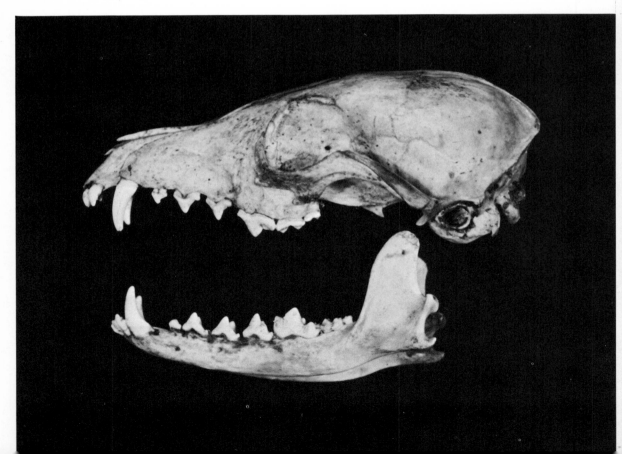

Meet the Red Fox

The red fox is classed as a carnivore because of its teeth, but it is often omnivorous because of circumstances and food preferences. Like all members of the Canidae, or dog family, the red fox has forty-two teeth: twelve incisors, four canines, sixteen premolars, and ten molars. The canine teeth are long, slender, and curved slightly to the rear. Although the red fox often feeds on mice, its teeth have been adapted by nature for grasping and killing much larger prey.

The first molars in both the top and bottom jaws are referred to as "carnassial" or "shearing" teeth. A fox swallows whole any piece of meat or food that it can get down. Larger pieces of meat must be torn apart or severed. To cut off a piece of meat, the fox turns its head sideways and uses its carnassial teeth, which work just like a pair of shears.

A red fox pup plays with a stick, turning its head sideways to use its carnassial teeth.

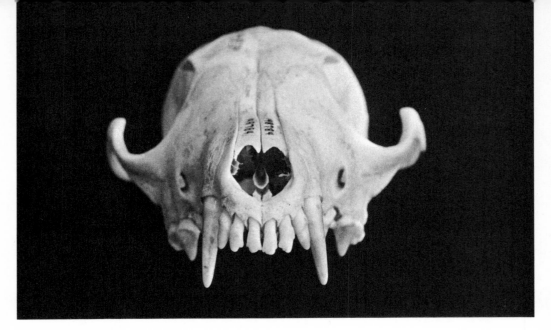

Note the lobed incisor teeth of the red fox.

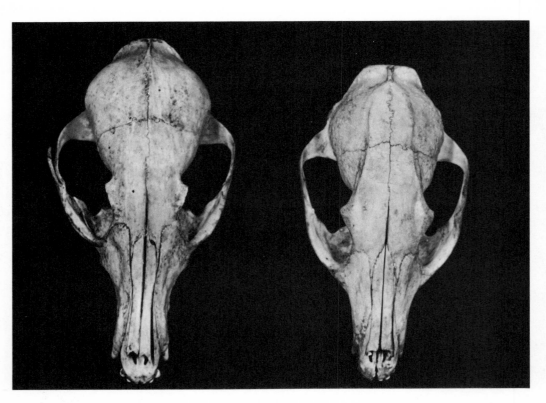

Note the narrow saggital crest on the red fox skull at left; the wide or lyre-shaped saggital crest on the gray fox skull at right.

Meet the Red Fox

Many people become angry when their dogs bolt food. They do not realize that this is the nature of all the Canidae. Members of the dog family have teeth adapted to grasping prey, killing it, and then cutting off pieces to be swallowed. The teeth are not efficient in chewing or masticating food; in the stomach there are powerful enzymes that soon break down the chunks of swallowed meat.

The upper incisors of a red fox are lobed, with tiny, rounded points. The gray fox's teeth do not have these lobes; this is a good means of distinguishing between the skulls of the two species.

Even better red fox identification marks are the temporal ridges on the top of its skull. They are rather indistinct and form a shallow V with the apex to the rear of the skull; the gray fox has very prominent paired ridges that form a U.

A red fox does not have a notch at the rear of its lower jawbone; the gray fox has a very prominent one.

The eyes of the red fox are at the front of its head, as are those of all of the carnivores. This placement of the eyes provides binocular vision,

Like all carnivores, this red fox pup has eyes on the front of its head, giving it binocular vision.

The eyes of this cottontail rabbit, as in most prey species, are on the side of its head, enabling it to watch for danger in all directions.

The elliptical pupils of this silver fox are characteristic of all foxes.

which is three-dimensional and essential to the fox in its pursuit and capture of its prey. Because the carnivores are not usually hunted by other animals, it is not so important for them to be able to see behind them as it is for the rodents and herbivores, which have eyes in the sides of their heads.

The foxes are the only members of the dog family that have elliptical eye pupils; all the others have round pupils. Bright light causes these pupils to contract to the narrowest of slits, a feature that resembles the pupils in the eyes of cats rather than those of the other wild dogs. The elliptical eye pupils in foxes may have evolved because they usually hunt all night, whereas the wolves and coyotes often hunt later into the morning and may begin earlier in the evening while there is still daylight.

I do not know if a fox can see better in the dark than a wolf or coyote, because all three animals have good eye reflectance that glows if a light is shined in their eyes. Who has not read of—if he has not actually seen—the light reflected from the eyes of one of these predators passing beyond the ring of light from a campfire?

Not only are the fox's eyes generously supplied with rod cells, which do most of the work of seeing in dim light; the fox also has a so-called "mirror" in each eye. Light reflected at night, however dim, passes through the retina and stimulates vision. Immediately the same light bounces off the mirror and passes back through the retina, allowing the light to be reabsorbed from the opposite direction. This increases the possibility of sight by 100 per cent, a great advantage to a predator that hunts in the dark.

The fox has good eyesight; it is quick to catch the slightest motion but often overlooks a motionless figure. Unlike a dog, which can recognize a man by his shape even though the man stands still, the fox often fails to do so. All the mammals except the primates are color-blind so that the fox views its world in varying shades of gray. Although the red fox has good eyesight and makes use of it, I am

27

A red fox squints to shield its eyes from the sun's brightness.

inclined to place sight third in importance among the fox's senses.

The erect ears of the red fox help give it its alert expression. The ears can be flattened against the head or turned slightly to point backward. The ears cannot be bent in the middle, nor do they ever droop.

The ears are also a key to a fox's emotions. When it is afraid or threatened, it flattens its ears against its head. If it is angry, it may make a threatening gesture by laying its ears backward but turning them slightly so that the black backs of the ears can be seen from the front. The darkened head pattern thus attained is more noticeable and is an aggressive sign.

Hearing is highly developed in the fox. It can hear a mouse squeal at about 150 feet if conditions are favorable. I have on several occasions seen a hunting fox stop, cock its head, turn aside from the direction it was traveling, and locate a vole a hundred feet away or more.

Tests on dogs have proved that what a man can hear at 175 yards, a dog can easily hear at a mile. Because of partial deafness, I wear a hearing aid, and when I turn it up I can hear sounds from farther away than most people can with normal ears. I also know that there are sounds loud enough to set both of my springer spaniels barking,

This red fox is alert, listening with ears cocked forward.

yet I cannot begin to hear them, even with the hearing aid. Though much prey comes to the attention of the fox through its ears, its hearing is not so important to it as its sense of smell.

Among humans the men who test perfumes are credited with having the keenest sense of smell. Through training and ability some of these men can identify hundreds of fragrances in varying amounts. Laboratory tests made by F. J. J. Buytendijk have shown that some highly trained dogs have been able to detect the odor of 1 part of sulfuric acid in a dilution of 10 million parts of water.

These tests have all been carried out under unnatural conditions on dogs that were used in laboratories. There is no doubt that the dogs had a highly developed sense of smell, yet they had been raised and fed by man. In other words, they did not have to depend on the use of their noses to secure food as a fox does. It would seem logical to believe that a wild fox would have the keener sense of smell.

I have often wished that people had the same keen sense of smell that wild creatures do. Perhaps it is just as well that we do not. An animal can practically psychoanalyze a person by his odor, thus easily detecting fear, frustration, anxiety, and sexual arousal.

We do know that many variables, such as heat, cold, moisture, wind, and barometric pressure, affect scenting conditions. Among the few animal odors that our sophisticated noses can distinguish are the unsophisticated odors of a wet dog or an angry skunk on a foggy night. At such times we may feel that we are wrapped in odor.

A fox is always wrapped in a world of odor. Invariably a fox hunts into the wind so that the scent of its prey is borne down the wind. When a fox is ready to lay up for the day, it circles into the wind, then lies down in a place where it can watch its back trail, while its nose will alert it to whatever is upwind.

Many advertisements for fox-trapping scents claim that Brand X will attract a fox a mile away. If such a scent happens to be placed ten feet downwind of the fox's path of travel and a strong wind is blowing, the fox will not notice it. If it is a warm, foggy night with no breeze stirring at all, the scent will flow downhill to fill up the hollows as if it were water. At such times, a fox could easily follow the trail of scent to its source for a distance of a mile.

One mammalogist following fox tracks in the snow saw evidence that a fox on three different occasions had passed 10 feet from roosting quail but did not discover them. Another mammalogist discovered that a fox had passed within 6 feet of a rabbit sitting in its form. In all four experiences the fox had passed on the upwind side and so had no chance to catch the scent.

Shrews, moles, and weasels are often killed by foxes but are seldom eaten. Often a fox won't even pick up such prey after it has killed it, because the musky odor, common to all three animals, is evidently distasteful to foxes. Foxes show that they do, however, have certain taste preferences by displaying an inordinate fondness for wild strawberries.

The sense of touch is much used by a fox. Watching one catch insects, we can easily observe that the fox is well aware of the insect that

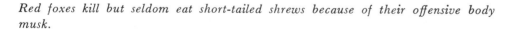

Red foxes kill but seldom eat short-tailed shrews because of their offensive body musk.

The right front foot of the red fox. Note the dewclaw, which is a fifth toe.

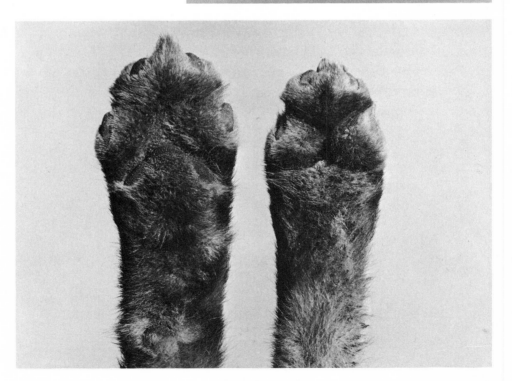

The front foot of the red fox is at left, the hind foot at right. Note the small toe pads, separated by lots of stiff hair.

it feels with its feet in the high grass. When a fox has become aware of traps, and their danger to it, and digs up the offending traps, its sense of touch informs the fox of the trap's exact whereabouts.

Whereas a deer walks on its toenails and a man walks on his entire foot, a fox is digitigrade and walks on its toes only. It is when a fox is lying down, sitting on its haunches, or carefully stalking its prey, with its belly almost touching the ground, that its heels come in contact with the ground. A fox has five toes on each of its forefeet, although only four toes show in the tracks because the fifth toe, corresponding to our thumb, is not so well developed and grows about 2 inches higher on the inside of the foot. Each hind foot has only four toes. The front foot is the larger, measuring about $1\frac{3}{4}$ inches long and 2 inches wide across the pads; the hind foot is $1\frac{1}{2}$ inches long by $1\frac{3}{4}$ inches wide. The hind foot from the toe tips to the heel is about 7 inches long.

The toenails vary in length from $\frac{1}{4}$ to $\frac{1}{2}$ inch and are slightly curved and nonretractable. They are worn down by contact with the earth. When a fox is running fast, it really digs in with its nails. I have often been able to track foxes by the nail marks when the dirt roadway was packed too hard to leave footprints. The claws are also used when the fox is digging to get at some of its prey, to make caches when burying its food, and to dig out or remodel its den.

The toe pads on a red fox are small and are separated by a dense growth of stiff hair. This is an adaptation to a cold climate, with the small pads preventing excessive heat loss. The hair not only provides insulation but ensures a better grip on smooth ice and prevents the pads from being cut on crusty snow. The small pads are a disadvantage in summer, because a fox loses moisture (perspires) through its pads and by panting. More heat could be discharged effectively if the toe pads were larger. The center pad of each foot is a thin transverse ridge, not large enough to project forward among the toe pads like that of a dog. On each hind foot there is a scent gland in front of this center pad.

Because a gray fox has much larger toe pads and a smaller foot than the red fox, it is usually easy to distinguish between the tracks of the two species.

Among our human population there is a significant percentage of people who find that it is frustrating to be left-handed in a world that caters to those who are right-handed. Foxes may not be frustrated, but 10 per cent of them are left-footed, as has been proved by the records kept by Joseph Taylor, predator control expert for the New Jersey Division of Fish and Game.

In his fox trapping, Joe had noticed that he usually caught the animal by its left front foot. Intrigued by his discovery, he kept careful records of the next 100 foxes he trapped and found that 90 of them were caught by the left front foot. All were taken in the dirt hole set, which is made in imitation of a hole naturally excavated by a fox and baited with a piece of meat. Approaching the hole, the fox would stand with its weight on its left front foot so that the right front foot could be used to remove the bait. The instinct of these foxes to use the right front foot to do the delicate job of removing the bait proved to Joe

The front foot of the gray fox is at left; the front foot of the red fox at right.

Taylor that 90 per cent of them were right-footed—the remaining 10 per cent were apparently left-footed foxes.

The fox has anal scent glands that are small, bluish, fatty lumps located just under the skin on each side of the vent. These glands mark the voidings of each fox with the individual's personal scent. On the top of the tail the red fox has another scent gland that is about 2 to 3 inches from the tail base. It is about 1 inch long and about ¼ inch wide. These glands are useful to the fox as a means of communication. They contribute to the "foxy" odor of the red fox, referred to as the "reek of a fox." Some people find this odor disagreeable, but I do not.

The fox seems proud of its tail, which is of great use to it. The tail is about 14 to 16 inches long and almost perfectly cylindrical, measur-

The red fox has a long, cylindrical tail.

ing up to 4½ inches in diameter from hair tip to hair tip. While walking or running, the fox carries its tail almost horizontally and uses it as a balance when turning sharp angles at high speed. When the fox is sleeping, its tail acts as a muff or a blanket and is used by the fox to cover its nose and feet. Among the "horsy" set of fox hunters, the fox's tail is called a "brush."

Occasionally a red fox may be born with an unusual tail. On March 8, 1955, George Tracy, Jr., of Niskayuna, New York, caught what appeared to be a three-tailed fox. Although only the regular tail had a vertebrae core, as a proper tail should, the other two were appendages of skin about 12 inches long that looked exactly like the real thing.

In the wild, the red fox has a potential life span of about ten to twelve years, although it is a rare fox that attains such longevity. The most accurate method of aging wild foxes is to live-trap them, put an identifying tag on them, and release them. This is an extremely slow and difficult procedure. X rays of the epiphyseal cartilage can be used to determine the fox's age up to two years, by which time the fox's wrist bones have fused together and no cartilage is visible. The apparent wear on the fox's teeth is also being studied and noted with an attempt to correlate a certain amount of tooth-wear to a definite age.

Rexford Lord, Jr., has experimented with age-determination of foxes by weighing their eye lenses. Lord's correlation between lens weights and age in cottontail rabbits has been successful and should also prove accurate for determining ages in foxes. Records of the length of life of foxes in captivity are accurate, and captive foxes usually live longer because they lead less hazardous lives. S. S. Flower reported in 1931 that one North American red fox male raised in the London Zoological Gardens lived for twelve years and twenty-one days.

My good friends Ralph and Fred Space, who own the Space Wild Animal Farm at Beemerville, New Jersey, had one red fox that lived to be sixteen years old, and a silver fox that holds the red fox longevity

The red fox carries its tail almost horizontally when walking or running.

A sleeping red fox covers its nose and feet with its tail.

record of eighteen years. In addition to raising foxes, minks, and keeping wild animals in captivity, the Spaces manufacture animal food. They credit the two foxes' long lives to the well-balanced, heathful diet that they had been fed.

Common usage may affix certain descriptive names to various types and sexes of wildlife. Some of these terms are limited, covering a specific situation, while others are so all-embracing as to be confusing. And so it is with terms applied to the fox.

The English have probably coined the greatest number of descriptive terms. They call a group of foxes a "skulk." I assume that this must be a family group, since foxes are not gregarious.

A male fox is often referred to as a "dog fox." I prefer to refer to it as just a male. Unless "fox" is always added to the word "dog," someone may confuse the issue with the common domesticated dog.

The female fox is referred to as a "bitch" or a "vixen." "Vixen" is much the better word to use because it is applied only to a female fox, whereas "bitch" is also used to describe the female domesticated dog.

A young fox is called a "cub," "whelp," "kit," or "pup." These terms are also used to describe the young of various other animals. The word "cub" is most frequently applied to the young of the bears, while "whelp" can be applied to a whole array of young animals. Many biologists use the word "kit" in talking of a young fox; yet since this is an abbreviation of the word "kitten," describing the young of the felines, its use is confusing. The word "pup" is used to describe the young of all the canines, be it wolf, coyote, or fox, yet when the majority of people think of the young of the fox they think of it as a fox pup, and this is the term that I prefer.

Spring

IN THE BEGINNING, baby red foxes are aware only of the warmth and presence of their mother and of each other. Their ears do not function properly, and their eyes are sealed shut. The darkness of the den is not a hindrance; they cannot see. As soon as each pup is born, the mother washes it thoroughly. The warmth and softness of her tongue are their first sensations. Although it will not be so later, touch is now their main link with life.

Driven by instinct, the pups, within minutes after their birth, seek their nurse. Attracted to her in their hunger for her warm, life-giving milk, each pup, twisting and turning on its belly, wriggles toward the mother to reach one of her eight swollen nipples. Tufts of her hair are grasped and then rejected by them. Eventually, because of their nursing, all the hair surrounding each nipple is pulled out or worn away. Grasping a nipple, each pup greedily fills its belly, relaxes its hold, then curls up and goes to sleep. This is to be each one's pattern of life for the next week, during which the mother is with them almost constantly.

Although a fox has strong, stout claws, it seldom digs a den of its own. Most fox dens are those that they take over from a woodchuck, a badger, or a marmot. The den may have been abandoned by these animals, or the woodchuck or the marmot may have been driven out and even killed and eaten by the fox. Usually the burrows of these dens are too flattened for easy use by the foxes, which enlarge them

Red foxes not only eat woodchucks; they also enlarge woodchuck dens for their own use.

so that the den hole soon has a higher ceiling or a definite O shape.

A fox den can be established almost anywhere, provided that the digging is easy and the foxes feel secure; however, an eastern, southeastern, or southern exposure of the burrow opening seems to be preferred. Many dens are in woodlands, or in open fields, some are along river bluffs or banks, a few may be among rock ledges, and an occasional one may be in a hollow tree. In some areas foxes prefer to den under old sawmill sawdust heaps and slash piles. They usually select a den that is on a knoll, because the knoll offers better observation and the burrow is better drained. Even in flat fields the foxes select a den that has been dug on a small eminence above the surrounding ground. Foxes prefer that the soil be sand, gravel, or light loam. Clay and hardpan soils are usually avoided by foxes because the digging is too difficult and drainage so poor that it is hard to keep the den sanitary. Yet in some regions the fox has no choice.

Many writers say that the fox's den entrance is hidden or concealed. It is my opinion, based on personal observation, that a red fox den is one of the most conspicuous of all wildlife. The foxes usually remove so much material from the den that they accumulate a large mound of dirt at several of the entrances. A few of these, broken out by the foxes in digging from below, may lack this mound; however, any grasses or other plants at these entrances are soon worn away. As the parent foxes bring in food, the entire area soon becomes littered with discarded bits of fur, bones, and feathers.

Joe Taylor could recall only one den that did not have a mound of dirt around its main entrance. This den was an old one that went down between the roots of a large tree, and the entrance was so big that it did not have to be further enlarged. Grasses had grown over the old excavated dirt after the den had been abandoned by its previous occupants.

Most of the dens have one or two main entrances and perhaps two or three less conspicuous plunge holes. The largest number of entrances that I have seen interconnected in one den is ten. Although there were three main entrances with large dirt mounds, one was preferred over the others and was used as a nursing mound. There were four lesser entrances with smaller but still conspicuous amounts of excavated dirt visible. Three additional holes had no excavated dirt in evidence. One of the lesser entrances had collapsed and was no longer being used. Well-defined trails through the grass and willows led from one entrance to another. Usually these trails are about 4 inches wide when used by the parents but become wider when the pups are playing about.

Adolph Murie, a naturalist in Alaska, reported one red fox den that had nineteen entrances. However, a den discovered by William G. Sheldon near Townsend, New York, on May 5, 1948, holds the record with twenty-seven entrances. It must be added that this den was also occupied by two different vixens and two different sets of pups. The two litters could be distinguished by the differences in the sizes of the animals.

Although red foxes have been generally considered to be territorial animals, there are enough records now to prove that, under certain conditions, tolerance between foxes in adjoining territories may be more common than was formerly acknowledged. Territorialism is extremely important during a food shortage because each pair of foxes needs whatever area it can hold against other members of its own species in order to secure enough food for its own pups. An over-abundance of foxes may force each pair to have a smaller range, and an abundance of food may negate the need of individual territory entirely. Under such conditions the use of one den by two pairs of foxes becomes more common.

In upstate New York, Sheldon also found foxes doubling up on living quarters near Newfield and at Ithaca. Walter Stairs, William Mosensteen, and Thomas Dolan, all of New York State, reported multiple families occupying a single den. Similar reports from Nelson

Swink in Virginia, D. F. Switzenberg in Michigan, and Charles Sheldon in McKinley Park, Alaska, suggest that multiple denning may be widespread. Both Lundberg and Hainard report two pairs of European red foxes denning together, and S. I. Ognev adds that this is common in the Siberian red fox.

These two separate dens 100 feet apart are used by one red fox family.

Not only do two vixens use the same den simultaneously, but they usually nurse and feed the pups indiscriminately. Nelson Swink also noted that if a fox den is disturbed or the litter scattered, other females will adopt the pups.

Red fox dens are usually widely scattered, but the abundance of food that allows multiple denning also permits, or induces, a concentration of dens in a small area.

Joe Taylor discovered two separate red fox dens, both of which were being used by two separate families, in one forty-acre field on the Baker farm near Stewartsville, New Jersey. He also knew of three dens ringing the dump on the outskirts of Washington, New Jersey, that were used every year. I know of two red fox dens about 800 feet apart near the Belvidere, New Jersey, town dump. In both of these, an unlimited supply of rats provided all the food the foxes could use.

William G. Sheldon's research turned up five different occupied fox dens in an area of 200 acres. Harvey I. Fisher, in Missouri, found six occupied dens about $1/4$ mile apart. However, these occurrences are unusual and suggest that red foxes are capable of adapting to unusual circumstances.

The entrance to a fox den is from 8 to 12 inches wide and about 15 inches high. The tunnel usually slants downward to about 4 feet beneath the surface and then extends laterally for 20 to 30 feet and resurfaces. Somewhere along the main tunnel is an enlarged chamber serving as the maternity den. No bedding is carried in as the sand or dust makes the floor sufficiently soft. Additional shafts extend from this main tunnel to the extra den openings. Rarely, there may be an interlinking network of tunnels. One den that was dug out by investigators extended downward to a depth of 14 feet.

The majority of the red fox pups are born around the middle of March after a gestation period of fifty-one days. Litter sizes vary from four to eight pups, with about six pups being the average. There is only one litter per year. Both the parturition, or birthing, date and the number of foxes in the litter may vary according to the latitude. Litters born in the north are usually later and smaller in number than those in the southern part of the red foxes' range. Individual foxes, because of physiological condition,* may vary greatly from both of these general accepted norms.

Biologists in Indiana doing research on the red fox examined a dead female which was pregnant at the time (January 2). No estimation was given as to the age of the fetuses, so I cannot tell when they would have been born. On February 14, Roy Welsh, of Charlotte, Michigan, shot a pregnant female red fox containing eleven well-developed embryos, but again the investigator did not estimate the ages of the embryos, so that no suggestion could be made as to the date on which they would have been born.

Don Purdy, of Ithaca, New York, found four red fox pups at the end of February that he estimated to be four weeks old. This means that the female had to be bred in the middle of December.

Joe Taylor provided me with the birth date of a litter that he had dug out of a den on the Richard Craig farm at Ludlow, New Jersey. On February 27, 1959, the vixen was tracked to her den in a large woodlot. That winter was very cold, and there had been a lot of snow with most of it lying on the ground until late in the spring. The den itself was very deep underground. There were seven pups in it, and Joe estimated that they were about three days old because the umbilical cord, although drying up, had not yet dropped off. This would

*Editor's Note: A number of conditions may affect the birth rate and numbers of young produced by a wild mammal. Generally, they operate in combination with one another, which makes it often impossible to isolate them under natural conditions. The age of the mother has a definite bearing on the number of young she produces per unit of time— the mother is usually more productive when she is younger, but as she ages the number of young in each litter may decrease. With mammals of more than one litter a year, the mother may produce fewer litters when she is older. Nutrition, or adequate food, for example, may greatly influence the frequency of births and the number of young in a litter, and with North American rabbits, tree squirrels, meadow mice, chipmunks, deer mice, shrews, and foxes, there is a statistically positive correlation between the sizes of litters and the geographic latitudes in which they are born.

mean that the vixen would have been bred about January 4. Joe also provided the latest spring whelping date by catching a red fox female on May 8, 1966, near Hackettstown, New Jersey. She was carrying in her uterus six fully developed pups.

I have no personal records of early birth dates of young red foxes because in studying and successfully photographing the pups, it was imperative that I did not disturb the dens. Eight is the largest number of pups that I have ever seen at a single den.

Joe Taylor's record of ten pups in one den was on the Long Range Gun Club property at Long Valley, New Jersey, and they had been born on March 12. Another friend, George Johnson, took excellent movies of twelve pups at one den in Sussex County, New Jersey. Roger Latham, the Outdoor Editor for the Pittsburgh Press, saw thirteen pups at one den in Montgomery County, Pennsylvania. Edward Keith, one of New York State's most famous fox trappers, reported fourteen pups at one den near Elizabethtown, New York. A fox den in Vernon County, Wisconsin, also had fourteen pups in it. D. F. Switzenberg, in 1948, reported two red fox dens in Michigan with fourteen and fifteen pups in each.

The largest litter of red foxes ever recorded was discovered by Larry C. Holcomb on April 20, 1956, in Calhoun County, Michigan. Holcomb found seventeen pups in one den. He based his conclusion that this was a single litter on the fact that the pups were all of one size and badly emaciated. A litter this large would have put a tremendous strain on the parents' ability to catch enough food to fill the needs of the pups. The fact that the pups were starving indicated that the task was beyond their capabilities and also shows why the average litter is much smaller.

An animal's reproductive rate tends to be sufficient to maintain the population of the species at the *status quo*. Availability of food, an increase in range and suitable habitat, and predation are just a few of the factors that have a direct bearing on the population of a spe-

Alaskan red fox pups venture out from their den.

cific creature at a specific time.

When I was in Alaska in the summers of 1965 and 1966, I was surprised to find that red fox litters there averaged about three pups each. At first I thought that this might be due to a shortage of food, although the summer supply of food, at least, was more than adequate. It should be noted that all the large litters recorded above were in areas that were heavily settled. Fox studies in Michigan showed that in the settled southern part of the state the litters averaged six pups each. In the wilder northern peninsula, the litters averaged five pups each. An increase of food in the rural sections apparently is not the reason for the larger litters because even in the Alaskan and Canadian wilderness the population, subject to cyclic changes, is holding steady. The foxes in the lower portion of their range are exposed to more adversity than those in the north. Thus, the foxes in Alaska have smaller litters not because of food shortages but because of an adaptation—the smaller litters can maintain the population of the species.

As her time of parturition approaches, the vixen begins to cache food in and around the den. The cool underground temperature of 56 degrees Fahrenheit deters spoilage.

The male and female fox have been inseparable for the past three months, and now there is a change in the female's habits. No longer does she join the male in his nightly forays, nor does she allow him in the den when he tries to seek her out. As they have been sharing in whatever prey they have caught, the male continues to leave a share of his catch at the mouth of the den. At last the whimpering cries of the newborn pups probably inform the male of what has taken place.

At birth the fox pups are 6 to 8 inches in body length and have tails 2½ to 3 inches long. Each hind foot is more than 1 inch long, and the ears, already erect, are about ½ inch long. The pups weigh about 4 ounces, with the males being slightly larger and heavier than the females. Richards and Hine in *Wisconsin Fox Population* give the sex ratio at birth as 52 per cent males to 48 per cent females. The heads of the pups are blunt because the muzzles are short; the eyes and ears are closed. A dark brownish-gray coat of fuzzy underfur covers the pups except for the soles of their feet. The tail already sports the characteristic white tip.

For about ten days after giving birth, the vixen stays in the den nursing and caring for the pups. This period, plus the few days before giving birth, is the longest that an adult red fox spends in the den. After the pups' baby-blue eyes open at nine days of age, the vixen begins to spend longer periods of time away from them.

The butterfat content of the vixen's milk is about 9 to 10 per cent, or about three times richer than the watery substance that we drink from dairy cows. On this rich food the young grow rapidly and their appetite grows apace.* With each passing day their size and strength increase, allowing the pups to begin to crawl about. Coordination is lacking at first, but this, too, develops with increased activity.

When the pups are about two weeks old, the vixen hunts for food in the vicinity of the den. The male, hunting much farther away, has now been accepted back into the family group. And at the risk of being accused of anthropomorphism, I will add that the female is happy to welcome him back.

While studying the red fox at one den for eight days in Alaska in 1966, I witnessed several meetings between the male and female fox that could be described with only one word—ecstasy. Both the male and the female were bringing in food to the den for the pups but were sleeping elsewhere. Because their visits did not often coincide, the two adults sometimes went two days without seeing each other. After one or the other of the adults had fed the pups, it would sit on the nursing mound and scan the horizon looking for its mate. The female came in more often and stayed longer so that she was usually doing the searching.

The female always saw the male coming before I did, but I instantly knew of his approach because the female's body would become taut and she would shiver in anticipation. As the male drew near, the female bounded out to greet him, uttering a loud, high-pitched wail.

Editor's Note: From analyses of the milk of at least nine orders of mammals—from marsupials to ungulates—it was discovered that the water, protein, fat, lactose, and ash content varied considerably between the wild mammals tested. There appears to be a correlation between the amount of protein in the milk and the growth rate of the young of certain wild mammals; however, more studies are needed before conclusions can be drawn with certainty. For example, human milk contains only 1.2 parts of protein per hundred, and it requires about 180 days for a human infant feeding on human milk to double its weight. The milk of the harp seal contains 11.9 parts of protein per hundred, and the baby harp seal doubles its weight in about five days. Much of the rapid gain in the weight of seals, however, is due to fat deposition and not to an increase in size. Richness of calcium and phosphorus in milk also appears to be related to peculiarities in the growth of young mammals.

A red fox scans the horizon for its mate.

The female red fox greets the male with her tail up over her back.

When she got close to him, she would flop down on her belly, raise her tail up over her back, and wave it furiously. From the prone position she would spring up and kiss the male all over with her tongue, and the male would reciprocate. The male would then pick up whatever food he had dropped during this exchange, and the pair would trot back to the den and the pups.

There is some evidence that at about this time the pups begin to eat regurgitated food, getting their first taste of meat. Joe Taylor reports a red male taking over the care of the pups after the female had been killed. As the pups were only two to three weeks old, the male would have had to feed them regurgitated food. Even a mouse would have been too much for the pups to have swallowed.

The only time that I ever saw a regurgitation was when the male fox "threw up" a couple of voles. As he approached the den, his mouth was empty so far as I could ascertain, and the pups characteristically bit and pulled at his mouth. With his head held low and his flanks heaving, he coughed up the two voles. Fox pups often looked as if they were "kissing" the adults, an action that I believe the pups engage in to stimulate the adults into regurgitating food for them.

Fox pups are noisy little creatures when very young. When the parents are away from the den either hunting or just lying out resting, the pups often whimper and whine. They frequently disclose their presence in the den by such sounds, since they can easily be heard from the entrance. As they grow older, they are evidently taught to be quiet, or at least they become quiet when they hear unfamiliar noises near the den.

At four to five weeks of age, the pups weigh about 1 pound 10 ounces and begin to poke their heads cautiously out of the den to look around. The great big outside world is a terrifying place, and the first fluttering of a leaf or the slightest noise sends the pups tumbling back down into the safe darkness in the womb of the earth. The pups, however, are an equal blend of caution and curiosity, and in a short time

These red fox pups are glad to see their mother.

the fright is forgotten and the furry little heads begin popping out again.

Meadow mice, or voles, are heavily hunted at this time of year. The sun is only now gaining the warmth needed to force the grasses, shrubs, and trees into new leaf. Last year's weeds and grasses fell before the ravages of the winter's storms, and the weight of the snow has impacted it into a shallow blanket. Beneath this thin covering the activities of the mice are readily seen, smelled, and heard by the predators. The adults as well as the pups eat quantities of these mice. Always a high percentage of a fox's diet, mice are the most frequently eaten food at this time.

Although cottontail rabbits are also raising their young at this time, fox predation on young cottontails is minimal. Foxes are also accused of breaking up the nests of ring-necked pheasants, and occasionally they do. Intense research, however, has cleared the fox of being anything more than a nuisance to pheasants. During the breeding season the cock pheasant becomes quite aggressive and even pugnacious and is extremely reluctant to flush. This hesitation may slow the pheasant's reaction to danger long enough so that occasionally one may be caught by a fox. The hen pheasant is usually very choosy about selecting a nest site and seeks out the densest cover she can find. As much heavy brush and vegetation are usually laden with dew at night, the fox avoids

Meadow voles are a favored red fox food.

such places because of its reluctance to get wet. The rare instance of a fox's eating the eggs of a pheasant does not necessarily affect the pheasant population because the hen invariably nests again. In fact, by hatching her brood at a later date, the hen may have more success in raising them, as the chicks will not be exposed to the chilling April showers. A disadvantage is that the pheasant's first clutch is her largest.

At six weeks of age, the pups are venturing out of the den when the parents come in to feed them. At this age they weigh about 2½ pounds and are much more alert than are dog pups. Centuries of domestication have taken their toll on the dogs, and their pups are not so precocious as are their wild kin, nor do they have to be. At eight weeks of age, the fox pups' eyes change color from blue to yellow.

At first the pups feel safe out of the den only when the parents are there. When either parent returns with food, it goes to the mouth of the den and utters a soft, murmuring "mmmmmmmmmmmm." Immediately the pups come tumbling up out of the den to be fed. If the parent has brought back a prey mammal or bird, the pups quickly seize it. When two or three of the pups grab the prey, a tug of war ensues. This pulling and tearing is accompanied by much growling, hissing, and whining. Sometimes a vole is actually pulled apart. The successful pup does not feed on his prize outside but quickly pulls it into the den and disappears from sight.

The vixen, after surrendering her prey, may flop down on the ground on her side and allow the remaining pups to nurse, which they do with gusto. As the pups grow older, the female more often nurses them while standing. The pups also attempt to nurse the male when he brings in food. They eagerly search through the hair on his belly and are perplexed when they cannot find the accustomed nipples. The male stands for just so much of this treatment before he strides away.

Nursing a growing family puts quite a drain on the female, and she soon becomes gaunt and worn. The gradually lengthening days expose the adult foxes to increased hours of sunlight, which bleaches their

A male red fox joins his pups at the den. The pups feel safe when a parent is with them.

Red fox pups pester a male red fox, looking for nipples to nurse.

coats to a light blond. With summer approaching, all the adult foxes are now shedding their long winter hair. The hair on the female's belly has been mostly worn off or pulled out by the pups in their nursing. The little hair remaining on her belly takes on a reddish tinge.

During this annual molt, the hair often sloughs off in large patches, and the animals take on a moth-eaten appearance. The dead hair must be quite irritating to the foxes because they often sit and groom them-selves with their teeth. This currycomb action pulls out mats of hair which, when dropped, retain the perforations of the fox's lower canine teeth.

The parents by this time are not spending much time at the den. They come in to feed the pups and then retire to sleep. The female comes in to feed the pups eight to ten times in a twenty-four-hour period; the male comes less frequently. The female hunts much closer to the den and lies up for the day a short distance away. The female often brings mice and voles as well as larger prey back to the den. Most of the feeding activity takes place between 5 and 10 A.M. and between 4 and 8 P.M.

After feeding the young, the male seldom stays around the den very long. The pups devil him so that he soon trots off to find a secluded spot where he curls up in the sun and goes to sleep. The female spends more time with the pups; however, because she is not hunting so far afield as the male, she is less tired. When hunting is poor as it usually is close to the den, the female may also eat some of the food provided by the male.

Although hunting is poorer near the den because of the increased hunting pressure of the adult foxes, this does not mean that they have killed off all of the prey animals in the area.

In Alaska, when I was working in a blind near a fox den in McKin-ley National Park, I was surprised to see voles occasionally run out of the grass and follow the fox trails to the den, scramble up over the entrance mound, and disappear in the grass beyond. In fact, I usually

As summer approaches, the red fox sheds its winter coat.

knew when a fox was in sight by heeding the alarm notes of a pair of
Lapland longspurs from a nearby nest. These birds always heard or saw
the fox long before I did and sounded the alarm. The longspurs are
ground-nesting birds, and this pair successfully raised their brood of
five young in a nest that was not more than 75 feet from the fox's den.
I always wondered why the foxes didn't associate the alarm call of the
parent birds with a nest of young ones. The foxes apparently didn't
care about the birds and didn't try to catch them, because if I could
find the nest, the fox certainly could have without any trouble. And yet I
saw the foxes hunt the longspurs when they were some distance away
from the den area.

57

A most unusual occurrence of this kind was witnessed by H. Gray Merriam at a fox den that was under observation near Cornell University in Ithaca, New York. On April 15, 22, and 25, he saw a large woodchuck entering the den that was being used by a vixen and her pups. In the narrow confines of the burrow, a large woodchuck could be a formidable opponent. The foxes had been feeding on woodchucks because their remains were strewn about the entrance to the den, 'but they did not feed on that one. Nor did they kill the large woodchuck that Nelson Swink saw inhabiting an occupied red fox den at Blacksburg, Virginia, in the spring of 1951.

Joseph Eaton, of Berwyn, Pennsylvania, topped this, however. While excavating a fox den, he found four separate nest chambers leading off from the main tunnel, all of them occupied. The first contained one male fox pup; the second, an adult female woodchuck with four suckling young; the third, one male fox pup; and the fourth, the red vixen and another male pup. I would say that the woodchuck was definitely pressing her luck. However, there are many things we see in nature that we can't really understand.

The pups first start to come out of the den only when they are called by the parents. After feeding, the pups usually play outside for a few minutes after the adults depart and then go back underground. As they grow older, they grow bolder and begin to spend a large part of the day playing outside.

Fox pups are almost constantly in motion. When one of them tires of play and wants to rest, the others won't let it. And so the activity goes on and on, like wind constantly stirring leaves.

The pups are vociferous and show their moods by barking, growling, whining, whimpering, snarling, hissing, and yapping. The tail, too, is an indicator of their emotions. When a pup is happy and contented with the world, it holds its tail high. In anticipation, it gives out shrill pitched yaps. If the pup is perplexed or puzzled, the tail starts to drop and the head is cocked to one side quizzically. When it is

A red fox pup cocks its ears, alert to some distant sound.

Red fox pups about two or three months old explore the area near their den.

angered or frightened, the ears are laid back and the tail is held low. This action usually precedes flight into the den.

A clear invitation to play is often given by one fox pup to another or to an adult. The pup crouches on its belly with its forepaws extended, its head lying on its paws, its tail wagging. From this position the pup can launch itself in a mock attack. Frequently it hits the other pup so hard that both are bowled over by the collision. Recovering, they throw themselves upon one another, biting and growling ferociously. These tussles are an open invitation to the rest of the pups, and they all pile in. Each cares little about which of its companions it bites. The game is to bite someone, anyone, and to tell the world about it by barking and growling. Inevitably, some pup soon gets hurt. With a whimper of pain, the injured one rolls over on its back, exposing its throat and belly and wagging its tail. This is a sign of subjugation common to all of the Canidae, or dog family. The submissive posture is immediately recognized by the other; it is honored, and the fight is over.

Fox pups play the universal games of tag, leapfrog, and hide-and-seek that are enjoyed by the young of most mammals, including man. They delight in playing with their mother, and she tolerates considerable mauling, pushing, and pulling. As the vixen stretches on the ground in the midst of her frolicking pups, contentment is apparent in her actions. The pups find this an ideal time to stalk and to pounce on her slowly wagging tail. At such times, when she doesn't want the pups to nurse, she lies on her belly. The pups, thwarted in their efforts to get at her nipples, climb all over her head and body and have a wonderful time doing so.

When none of its littermates want to romp, a pup may toy with a stick, a leaf, or a bit of bone, although a stick seems to be preferred. The pup carries the stick about, tosses it in the air, pounces on it, and chews it. Nothing seems quite so satisfactory as a good stick. When a pup finally works off its excess energy, it stretches out on its belly with its hind legs pointing to the rear. In this awkward position, it can cool its belly against the earth and relax contentedly.

Red fox pups play actively and noisily.

All play is a conditioning for later life, and in the world of wildlife it is the fittest that usually survive. The stamina, strength, and coordination that the fox pup develops through play will be put to daily use as long as it lives.

The vixen starts to wean her pups when they are about two months old. The pups still try to nurse, and they annoy their mother constantly. She either lies down on her nipples or walks away if the pups attempt to nurse while she is standing. The increased size of the pups and their larger appetites, coupled with a decrease in their milk allotment, mean that much more food must now be brought in by the adults to feed them. Under ordinary conditions the parent foxes do this easily, for they are diligent hunters and food is plentiful at this season.

In addition to rabbits and meadow voles, the adult and young foxes feed on red squirrels, gray squirrels, flying squirrels, chipmunks, woodchucks, deer mice, and an occasional game bird.

Warden Lowell Thomas of Maine was on patrol one morning and noticed a red fox carrying something in its mouth. When the fox was close, Thomas shouted and startled the fox into dropping its load. The vixen had a rabbit, two woodcocks, and a red squirrel that it was taking

A red fox pup cools off by pressing its belly against the earth and panting.

A red squirrel barks an alarm at a red fox. Red squirrels are sometimes caught by foxes.

back to its young. Joseph Taylor, in checking his traps, found one sprung. Off to one side in a neat heap lay three voles. From the tracks it was evident that a red fox had been returning to its den to feed the pups when it caught the odor of Joe's bait. The fox had laid the voles down to get the bait and had almost been caught instead. Jerking back, the fox had been able to pull out of the trap but had been too unnerved to retrieve its voles.

Poultry allowed to run loose proves a tempting and tasty addition to the fox diet, although the fox often passes up a nearby flock to prey on those at a greater distance from the den. It is as if the fox wanted to keep peace with its human neighbors. I first realized this when I discovered a couple of fox dens on our home farm. The remnants of chickens that were strewn around were all white Leghorn while we raised Rhode Island Reds. The fox had to go almost ½ mile farther to get the Leghorns than it would have had to go to get our birds.

At times a fox becomes bold and takes poultry even though the farmer is within sight. Mr. Lance, of Springtown, New Jersey, was raking in his garden when he heard a gagging-honking sound. Looking up, he saw a red fox dragging off a goose that had been sitting on its nest. The goose was too heavy for the fox to carry, and the terrorized

63

bird was fighting with its wings. Mr. Lance, who was seventy, ran after the fox with his rake but couldn't catch the fox, which ran backward, pulling the goose along by its neck.

A fox is an opportunist, and it is quick to take advantage of any food item that it can find or catch. It does considerable scavenging and carries home any prize it discovers. One of the fox dens near the Washington, New Jersey, town dump contained almost two bushels of soup bones that had been retrieved from the dump. It is not likely that there was any meat left on the bones when the fox found them, but their odor was probably irresistible.

Many times sportsmen are quick to blame the fox for killing all the creatures whose remains are found at the den. This is jumping to conclusions. It is very difficult to tell by looking at an old chicken wing whether the fox killed the bird or picked it up as carrion. Who can prove that the rabbit was not killed on the highway by an automobile? In Alaska I found the legs of a caribou calf at a fox den. The legs had been scavenged from a calf that I knew had been killed by wolves.

I know of one red fox den that had remnants of two white-tailed fawns near the entrance. The fox didn't kill those fawns because I was aware that they had died of starvation after their mother had been killed on the highway. That particular den was surrounded by a large, varied collection of debris. In addition to the fawn carcasses, there were thirteen sets of Buff Coachin bantum chicken legs, parts of a muscovy duck, pieces of a white Peking duck and a barred Rock rooster, and a seven-pound jack rabbit. Pieces of cottontail rabbits, hen and cock pheasants, and wings and feet of almost fifty small birds such as red-winged blackbirds, meadowlarks, flickers, and bobolinks were scattered about. The adult foxes probably killed most of these creatures, but we cannot be sure. As Paul Errington reported, "The cured ham that some Iowa hunters retrieved from a fox den does not indicate that the fox killed a pig."

The remains of mice are seldom found around the den because they are small enough to be eaten whole. Mice remains do show up in the fox scats.

Carrion beetles are attracted to the carcasses and remnants of left-over prey strewn around the fox den. As these are easily caught, the pups add them to their diet. Vultures often drop down to share in whatever leftovers they can garnish at the den.

In June wild fruits start to ripen, and the foxes feed on the straw-berries, blueberries, and shadbush berries. Since the pups sample just about everything, they eat some of the various grasses that grow around the den. The adult foxes, too, often eat some grass, although probably more for its laxative properties than for its taste or food value.

A scavenged caribou calf leg lies outside a fox den in Alaska.

A red fox pup about two or three months old hunts about.

As the pups grow older, the parents start dropping the food farther and farther from the den. In this way, the young are lured from the den and start hunting for their own food.

While the foxes are busy hunting food for their young, other predators are similarly engaged. The pups' daily expansion of their horizons by venturing farther and farther from the sanctuary of the den is in direct proportion to their increased exposure to danger. The circling speck high in the sky can materialize within seconds into a plummeting eagle. Usually these rapacious birds are interested only in the pups, but there are two records of a golden eagle's attacking an adult fox. The pup that is out in the twilight hours is exposing itself to an attack by the great horned owl.

In the forested areas the bobcat, the fisher, the lynx, and the wolverine will quickly add a fox pup to their diet whenever they can capture one. The bobcat and fisher will take a pup only if the adult fox is not near; the lynx and wolverine will also kill the adults. The large predators such as the bear, the mountain lion, the coyote, and the wolf will kill a fox if the opportunity presents itself, but they do not ordinarily seek them out. A fox is particularly fearful of a wolf.

66

Spring

On two different occasions while I was working with red foxes in Alaska, I saw evidence of this fear. In the first, the female fox was out hunting, and in the other, the male was curled up in a gully sleeping. In both cases the fox suddenly became alert, and pausing only for a moment to look off in the distance, it streaked up over the hills and was soon out of sight. Straining to see what had caused such panic, I saw wolves trotting over the tundra. I still do not know what warning the foxes received when none was discernible to me. As foxes often feed on abandoned wolf kills, they lead a precarious existence.

In rural areas, the fox's most dangerous adversaries are the farmer and his dog. Farm dogs are usually allowed to run free at all times, and many of them hunt constantly. An adult fox has nothing to fear from a dog, but the dog might catch a fox pup. The dog's excited barking

A great horned owl feeds on a gray squirrel.

Red foxes are deathly afraid of the gray wolf.

at a fox den may bring the farmer out to investigate. Even if there were no debris around, the farmer could recognize the den by its foxy odor and the enlarged entrances. The typical reaction of most farmers, on discovering a den, is to return with traps and a gun, or a shovel to dig it out, or a tractor and a hose with which to pump carbon monoxide into it.

Young foxes learn what is dangerous from their parents' reactions to any circumstances. It is their nature to be timid and to be cautious about anything that is new. When the adults are alarmed, they give a coughing bark which signifies danger and the young disappear into the den. If a person approaches a den and some of the pups are playing outside, the parents may stay hidden nearby, but the sound of their alarm call will be heeded by the pups. Alan Devoe tells of a fox pup that was straying from the den. The mother became concerned and sat upright rigidly watching the pup, but she did not utter a sound. Gradually, the pup stopped and turned. Seeing the mother watching it, and sensing that something was wrong, the pup hurried back to safety.

68

Spring

Rarely the parent fox may become belligerent in defense of its young. One man had a fox dash at him and bark excitedly. With the fear of rabies flashing through his mind, he quickly left the area. Later he discovered the den nearby.

Foxes have been known to try to decoy danger away from the den. The parent fox often stands within sight of a dog and lures the animal into chasing it. In this way it can lead the dog from the den. It also uses this same ruse on humans. A farmer near Albion, Pennsylvania, told of a female fox that acted injured and kept trying to lead him away every time he approached an old pile of sawmill slash in which he knew she had her den.

Most foxes know of every den and burrow in their range and have two or three into which they can move if their maternity den is discovered and molested. Soon after the threat to the den, the parents move the pups to another. If the pups are small, the adults carry them in their mouths, sometimes by the head, at other times by the middle of the body. If the pups are large enough to walk, the female leads them to the new den. Some foxes have been known to split up the litter and carry the pups to two different, widely separated dens. Foxes sometimes move from one den to another if the first one becomes infested with parasites. Even though the foxes are unmolested, they seldom use the same den two years in succession.

William G. Sheldon reported several cases during den shortages in an area in New York State in which the foxes moved their litters in with another fox family.

Statistics show that the average person in the United States moves five times in his lifetime. One red fox family did a lot more moving than that—a total of eleven times in a three-month period.

Summer

DURING THE LANGUID DAYS of June the sun, a golden, burning orb, travels its longest arc across the sky. Shadows are shorter at noon because only at this time of year is the sun directly overhead. Although these are the longest days, the earth has not yet absorbed the heat which it will radiate in its greatest intensity in August. The earth still retains enough moisture from the showers of late spring to foster phenomenal vegetative growth. Each plant reacts like a magical beanstalk and soars to claim its rightful place in the sun.

June is a comparatively quiet month. The tumultuous bird songs that had greeted the dawn in May have lessened; birds are now engaged in the ever-demanding task of securing and cramming food into the gaping maws of their young.

July is more actively noisy as the hosts of sound-producing insects begin to mature, but it is during August that their cacophony of sound reaches a crescendo. During the day, shimmering heat and a multitude of sounds roll out like an enveloping wave. The air is filled, reverberates, pulses with the stridulations of katydids, crickets, and grasshoppers. Darkness brings no cessation, and only a lowering of the temperature can reduce the orchestration.

Across the continent, the fox pups, without knowing or caring, will find that these days of their first summer, while their parents provide

Life is easy for the red fox pups during their first summer.

both food and protection, are the easiest they will ever experience.

The pups learn to hunt as an adjunct to their play. When they come out of the den in the morning, they gambol about, fighting and tussling with one another. They pick up and carry sticks, bones, and whatever pieces of food scraps lie about. At once the scavenger beetles, crickets, and other arthropods that had sought shelter beneath the scraps scramble for new cover, since the pups pounce on anything that moves. Some of the larger beetles may be played with before they are eaten. The pup pins down the beetle with a paw and then stands back to watch the beetle reactivate itself. Again the paw flashes out to stop the beetle's progress, and again the paw is withdrawn. Sometimes the pup rises up on its hind feet, then pounces forward, using both front feet, to trap the hapless beetle with a motion that the fox will use constantly in later life to catch mice.

Pups learn to associate certain odors with food as they eat the prey brought in by the parents. As the pups grow, the adults often drop the food away from the den to force the pups into seeking it. Gradually,

71

the pups begin to hunt for food on their own near the den. Later they accompany the parents on their foraging expeditions.

In summer foxes eat great quantities of insects. The pups eat them because at first they are about all that a young fox can catch. The adults eat them because they are so plentiful, and the fox always eats whatever is most available and palatable. After a rainstorm or at night, earthworms are picked up and eaten. Leopard, pickerel, and wood frogs provide additional food, but the pups avoid toads after their first encounter. The very bitter, mildly toxic oil secreted by the glands on the toad's back causes the fox to release the toad as soon as it is caught. Slightly nauseated, the fox pup runs its tongue along the ground in an effort to free its mouth of the noxious taste.

The foods of the fox vary according to the area where it lives. The summer food of the red fox in the Far North is composed of many lemmings, voles, the young of ptarmigans, and varying hares. Almost half of the diet of the foxes in Alaska's interior is Alaskan ground squirrels. Foxes living along Alaska's coasts feed on sea urchins, clams, mussels, beach fleas, dead fish, and sea birds such as dovekies,

A female red fox brings an arctic ground squirrel to her pups in Mount McKinley Park, Alaska.

A muskrat rears back into a fighting position, ready to defend itself. Foxes often prey on muskrats.

puffins, murres, guillemots, auklets, and gulls. Sometimes the hunting habits of the foxes make entire areas untenable for sea birds.

Along Maryland's Eastern Shore, red foxes invade the marshes to feed on the muskrats, and some foxes swim out to the islands and establish their dens there. Often the drying up of the marshes coincides with the dispersal of some of the young muskrats that are setting out to establish home ranges of their own. These young animals are particularly vulnerable to fox attacks. Muskrat remains were found in 39 per cent of the fox scats gathered around the Blackwater marshes in Dorchester County, Maryland. A red fox that was shot in St. Louis County, Minnesota, had five young muskrats in its mouth.

In 1939 a prolonged drought in Iowa reduced the total muskrat

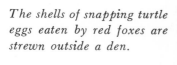

The shells of snapping turtle eggs eaten by red foxes are strewn outside a den.

Bobwhite quail make up a very small part of a red fox's diet.

population so severely that no muskrat trapping was allowed that year. With the marshes almost devoid of water, killing of muskrats by all predators increased greatly. Whereas under ordinary conditions predation by great horned owls and foxes would have been minimal, it became excessive—a case of the predator taking advantage of an unusual situation.

In the southern part of its range, the red fox in summer feeds on quail, cotton rats, and rice rats. In the Western states, the many ground squirrels, such as the thirteen-lined, Richardson's, California, and rock squirrels, are staples. In the mountains, the red fox ranges as high as the timber line, where it preys on the golden-mantled, Uinta, Columbian, and Belding's ground squirrels, as well as on marmots. In spite of what appears to be irrefutable evidence of tremendous fox predation, scientific studies have proved that foxes do not suppress any game species, especially in the summer, when there is so much other food available.

Across the continent, the gooseberry, crowberry, blueberry, black-

74

berry, serviceberry, saskatoon berry, and mulberry are avidly eaten by foxes. Occasionally foxes visit melon patches as well as fruit orchards. They usually hunt the orchards for mice but eagerly eat fallen plums and peaches. Some foxes even develop a taste for sweet corn.

This is a period of increased food consumption, brought about by the fox pups' greater size and activity. This is also the time when many poultry farmers are putting their pullets out on summer range before installing them in the laying houses. Most poultry predation by foxes in the past has been the result of poor poultry management. Today, most poultry farmers incinerate their dead birds to prevent the spread of any possible disease, whereas a decade ago most chickens that died would be thrown out into the fields. These discarded birds were a bonanza to the foxes, which gathered such carrion and carried it to the den to feed to their pups. But the discarded birds also accustomed the foxes to a taste for chickens in the area. If there were no dead birds to be had, the foxes could easily catch a live one.

Broiler production is such a science today that poultry farms are often referred to as factories. Chickens raised under such conditions are mass produced and never get out of a building until they are killed, dressed, and on their way to market. In some areas fox predation on chickens actually helped force such conditions.

Leo Saloski, a poultryman of Rosemont, New Jersey, had excessive poultry losses due to foxes. Mr. Saloski used to keep about 30,000 chickens and often had 10,000 on range at one time. He erected high fences, but the foxes either climbed over the fences or dug beneath them. He found that floodlights installed to bathe the area with light all night long were no deterrent. Neither were the dogs which he chained in the area, for the foxes soon learned that the dogs were chained and also knew the length of the chains. When dogs were allowed to roam loose, the foxes sneaked in while the dogs were elsewhere. Electrified fencing did help, but the losses were so great that eventually Mr. Saloski raised all the chickens in houses throughout the year.

Farmer Trieber, of Frenchtown, New Jersey, had a farm near a bluff that fell away to the Delaware River below. The bluff was so steep that it discouraged any but the most determined ascent by man; however, it supported a rank growth of plants. This produced a situation that was ideal for foxes, which had numerous dens on the bluff. To reach a food supply, the foxes had only to sneak up over the cliff, catch a chicken, and then retreat to their dens, where they were comparatively safe from pursuit. Trieber raised 300 more chickens than he needed because the foxes annually took a toll of about that number.

It is good general farming practice to rotate the crops so that clover, alfalfa, and other legume crops can restore the nitrogen to soil exhausted by previous corn crops. It is also good poultry practice to move the chickens to new range each year to prevent a build-up of chicken parasites in the soil. The drawback to this system is that it often puts a standing cornfield next to the poultry range, and the foxes are quick to take advantage of the protective cover provided by the corn.

Ralph Perry, who had a poultry farm on the outskirts of Washington, New Jersey, found the remains of over 200 chickens scattered about in a field of corn that joined his poultry range. Amos Smith, who lived nearby, had similar heavy losses. Fred Kayser, whose farm was on Montana Mountain, New Jersey, was particularly vulnerable to loss from fox predation because his farm was in an extensively wooded region. Hundreds of chicken remains were found in his cornfield, and when the state trappers were called in, they caught nine red and gray foxes in that one field in a week.

Fox predation helped shape the course of my life. The farm where I was raised was in the mountains, and heavy brush rows surrounded each field. A fox could move anywhere on the farm, its activities hidden because the cover was so heavy and unbroken. Our poultry losses were exceptionally high each season, although we never knew just how high until the birds were moved in from the range to the laying houses.

Although I had always trapped, as most farm boys do, these losses forced me to concentrate on foxes. The trapping of foxes is an art, and the procedure was long and slow; but I did master it. In the process, the constant study of wildlife and its habits became of much greater interest to me than farming, so eventually I gave up farming. Increased knowledge of wildlife finally allowed me to stop trapping and to devote my time to photography and to writing and lecturing about all types of wildlife. I am a professional naturalist today because the foxes ate my chickens.

Much of this predation on chickens in early summer is by the adult foxes securing food for their young. In late summer, much of the predation is by young foxes that find it easier to catch a domesticated bird than to catch a wild one. Ordinarily, a fox kills a single chicken and carries it off. Occasionally, however, the fox may go berserk and slaughter far beyond its needs. Three young red foxes ran into a chicken yard in Ringoes, New Jersey, about 5:30 one afternoon in August. In a matter of a few minutes, the foxes had killed thirty-five leghorn pullets, escaping with three of them. Paul Errington, a scientist who often studied foxes, reported one Iowa farmer who lost 160 chickens in two days to a red fox family. The chickens were just killed and left lying about, though undoubtedly several had been carried off to be used as food. Foxes usually carry their prey away from the spot where it is caught.

Joe Taylor told me of a gray fox he trapped at the New Jersey State Game Farm that had killed pheasants in excess of its needs. To get to the pheasants, the fox had to climb a 2-inch-thick mesh chicken wire fence that was 8 feet high. The first night the fox killed twenty-one pheasants; the second night it did not return; the third night it killed forty-two pheasants; and the fourth night it was trapped before it could do any more damage. Oddly, the fox had blue eyes, usually a feature of a very young fox. A red fox invaded the state game farm at Gray, Maine, and killed ninety-five pheasants. The fox was still killing pheasants when it was shot.

77

By the time the foxes are four months old, their milk teeth have been replaced by permanent teeth. At two months their guard hairs have started to push through the underfur; and at four months, they are well furred. The pups then weigh about six to seven pounds and are two-thirds grown.

At this age, the den is seldom used unless the young fox is chased by a dog. As the pup still does not have its full growth and strength, it tires easily and will then seek out the den as a sanctuary. When the pups were younger, they could be approached at the den. Now the sight of a man walking causes them to run to cover. If the foxes have been raised in a farm field, they have probably become accustomed to the farmer's tractor and do not associate it with danger. Even at four months of age, they can still be approached fairly closely as long as the man stays on the tractor and does not shut off the motor.

A young red fox sleeps in the sun in midsummer. Even after the fox family has split up, the young come back to the old den.

As the fox family grows older, the maternity den is abandoned and the pups follow the parents farther afield in their hunting. Other dens may be used as temporary residences, but by the middle of summer all the foxes are following what will become a lifelong habit of sleeping in the open. A hard rainstorm may force them to seek shelter for a few hours, but as soon as it is over the foxes are out and away. Quite frequently, as soon as the foxes abandon their dens, woodchucks take up residence in them.

The fox pups still play and fight among themselves, but the fighting becomes a lot rougher. Occasionally a fox's tail tip is lost in these skirmishes. The pups don't have as much time to play as they formerly did because they are more often engaged in the serious business of feeding themselves. Still, a red fox never seems to lose its desire to play. Even adults play by themselves, tossing sticks about or chasing after insects they are not really interested in catching. Foxes seem to get great enjoyment out of lying on their backs and wriggling about on the grass. This is also a grooming procedure that helps keep the fur bright and clean.

Red foxes have been seen playing with other animals. Charles Sheldon watched a red fox playing with Dall sheep in McKinley National Park. The fox ran around the sheep and jumped up and nipped at their faces. The rams gently butted the fox out of their paths with their heads. The red fox has been known to play with cattle, caribou, and elk in the same manner. Sometimes these large ruminants chase around after the fox in a game of tag, with both of them apparently getting enjoyment out of it. When the large animals lie down to chew their cuds, the fox has been seen to walk in among them and curl up and go to sleep. It is often thought that a fox associates with some of these herd animals in order to feed on the voles and lemmings disturbed and driven ahead of the passing herd.

On rare occasions, a fox establishes a friendship with a dog, and the two seem to enjoy playing together. There is even one record of a red fox pup playing (?) with men. Golfers at an exclusive country club outside Philadelphia, Pennsylvania, began complaining to the manager that a fox was running off with their golf balls. Whenever a ball was driven near a certain copse of woods, a young fox ran out, picked up the ball, and dashed back to cover. When the fox was shot, it was discovered that it had garnered a goodly supply of golf balls and many of the golfers had garnered extra strokes.

The conditioning that results from the playing and the increased dependency on its own food-catching abilities lengthen and strengthen the fox's muscles. Its lung capacity increases; a fox can run for hours without becoming exhausted. Our forefathers appreciated a fox's running ability, and an old-time remedy for asthma prescribed that the sufferer eat the lungs of a fox.

A red fox is very fleet, and the epitome of grace when it moves. It is so light and wraithlike that it moves like thistledown blown along by the wind.

A fox that is not going any place walks. I know that this may seem an odd statement, but a fox is not a walker. If it is loafing about at the

A red fox trots briskly through the grass. Foxes walk only when they are taking a few steps from place to place.

den and merely wants to move a couple of feet, it walks and its tracks are about 9 to 10 inches apart. But if the distance is any greater than that, the fox trots, and it can trot and trot and trot, seemingly forever.

When a fox trots, it travels about 5 miles an hour. When I was working with foxes in Alaska, I had many opportunities to follow those that trotted along a dirt road. I found that by walking as fast as I could, like a heel-and-toe walker, I could keep up with the fox. I have since timed that trot with a car's speedometer and found it to be about 5 miles an hour.

The tracks of a trotting red fox resemble a dotted line.

The tracks of a loping red fox are clearly visible in the snow.

In trotting, a fox's right front foot and left hind foot strike the ground at the same time. The left front foot and the right hind foot are then brought forward and placed on the ground in unison. Because the fox has such a narrow chest, its feet are placed almost exactly one in front of the other, leaving a track, when walking or trotting, that looks like a dotted line. With most trotting animals, you do not see the track of the front foot because the hind foot comes down on the spot that has just been vacated by the front foot. Animals that stalk their prey, such as the members of the cat family and foxes, are exceedingly careful walkers, and their hind feet cover each front track exactly. When trotting, each track is about 14 to 16 inches apart.

When the fox loped, I couldn't begin to keep up with it, even when I ran. The only reason I was able to keep the fox in sight was its habit of constantly stopping to hunt for something that had caught its attention.

82

A loping fox moves with a very smooth rocking-horse motion. The feet are placed in a sequence, with the left front foot coming down first, then the right front foot, and then slightly in front of those tracks the left hind foot followed by the right hind foot. Then there is a break in the tracks as the fox's body moves ahead and the sequence is repeated.

When hard pressed, the red fox bounds or gallops and is one of the fastest land animals in North America. In this gait, the fox's left front foot strikes the ground, followed by the right front foot, then the right hind foot lands, and the left hind foot completes the cycle. The fox, bounding alternately, arches and then extends its back, getting as much as 20 feet between strides, although usually less. The head is carried forward, the ears lie back, and the tail floats out straight behind. If the fox has to make a sharp turn at high speed, it whips its tail to the opposite side as a counterbalance. When the fox is loping or galloping, all four feet leave tracks.

Ernest Thompson Seton told of a red fox that ran at 30 miles an hour for half a mile in front of his automobile. Dr. Schrenkeisen clocked a red fox doing 45 miles an hour in front of his car. It has been pointed out that this is faster than a race horse runs. Harold A. Morton, of Winstead, Connecticut, and a friend also had to drive their car at 45 miles per hour to stay even with a red fox.

From my personal experience, I have had a red fox run ahead of my car at about 35 miles an hour. The fox did not run down the road long enough to give me a good accurate extended distance reading, but at 35 miles an hour I held steady with it. Although this is a good speed, I do know that the red fox can do better than that.

In 1946 a deer drive was held on the Hercules Powder Company's land in Belvidere, New Jersey. The entire area was fenced in, and the deer inside the enclosure had multiplied to the point where they were destroying all the plant life. A large section of the fence was taken down to allow the deer to escape, and about 150 of the local sportsmen

A red fox gallops at full speed.

Tracks of a galloping red fox show that all four feet are grouped when galloping.

turned out to act as drivers. The drive was a failure because the deer in their panic could not find the opening, which they did not know was there. You can never actually drive deer anyway; you just stir them up and they go where they want to.

A deer running at full speed, as these deer were doing, can run at about 35 miles an hour. During the drive, a red fox was started out of cover between John Steinhardt and me. Although the deer were running at full speed, the fox easily overtook and outdistanced them. The fox ran so fast it appeared to flow downhill and across the flat. In spite of the confusion taking place all around, the fox knew exactly where it wanted to go and slipped out of the area by sliding under the chain link fence in its customary spot.

Because of their great running speed, foxes are killed less often on highways than are most other animals. A fox's reactions are also quicker than those of most other animals, and they do not remain transfixed on the spot when a car's lights are shined in their eyes.

A fox sweats or perspires through the soles of its feet and by panting. By panting very rapidly, the heat of the body is discharged through the lungs, and cooler, fresh air is pumped in. Apparently this does not get rid of the heat as fast as it should because I have found that a fox that has been exerting itself strenuously has small air bubbles under the skin. A fox also attempts to lower its body temperature by drinking water, which it laps up with its tongue like a dog.

Red foxes dislike getting wet because their fur is not waterproof and, being so long, retains a lot of water and extra weight, especially in the tail. However, the fox can swim well and has been clocked at a swimming speed of 4 to 5 miles an hour.

The gray fox and the red fox are very different in habits and in habitats. The gray fox likes to live in dense cover such as swamps, heavy undergrowth, or around rock ledges. It doesn't like to run and, if pursued by dogs, it soon goes underground in a burrow or climbs a tree. It can climb well, and I have seen a gray fox shinny up a black

A red fox drinks water from a stream.

birch tree that had no branches lower than 15 to 20 feet above the ground.

The red fox prefers more open country and actually seems to enjoy running ahead of dogs. Some red foxes have been known to deliberately tease dogs into a chase. The red fox depends on its speed and its cunning, and it seldom holes up and rarely climbs. The only instance of a red fox climbing that I know of occurred in Russell Hoffman's peach orchard in Port Murray, New Jersey, in 1956. Hoffman heard his dog barking continuously in the orchard and went to investigate. To his surprise, he saw a red fox in the uppermost branches of one of

A red fox bites an itch.

his peach trees. Although the first limb was about 4 feet above the ground, the fox could have easily jumped that high and then climbed from branch to branch to get to the top so that this is not really an example of true climbing ability. The fox apparently had been surprised in the tree when the dog came by, because if it had been on the ground, it would not have climbed for safety but would have simply outrun the dog.

Given a chance, the red fox can outrun most of its enemies, yet some of its most deadly ones are so insidious that the fox is not even aware of them. I am referring to parasites and diseases.

The large external parasites are as evident to the fox as they are to man. The same parasites often affect both the fox and man. Various flies, mosquitoes, and midges are miniature Shylocks, each striving for its "pound of flesh."

The brown dog tick in the Southern states, the wood tick in the Eastern states and Canada, and the Rocky Mountain spotted fever tick in the Western states are the most common large bloodsuckers. These ticks frequent high, grassy areas and leap on the first fox or other warm-blooded creature that passes by. After becoming engorged with blood, the ticks drop off.

Fleas, lice, and mites do more than just torment the foxes. Some-

87

times the fox has such a heavy infestation of these pests that death ensues. This is particularly true of foxes that have mange mites, *Sarcoptes scabiei vulpis*. The sarcoptic mites burrow into the fox's skin and feed on the tissue just beneath the surface. The fox, greatly irritated, scratches at the spot, breaking the skin and causing further infection, lesions, pus, and scabs. In extremely heavy infestations, the fox is almost devoid of hair, and its body is covered with running sores. Under such conditions, the fox gradually becomes too weak to hunt, begins to starve, and finally succumbs.

In 1946-47, the State of Pennsylvania did a thorough study on the fox skins that had been submitted for bounty. Health officials checked 60,846 red foxes and 55,706 gray foxes. Of these, 780 red foxes had mange as compared to only two gray foxes. Late August was the peak month for this irruption. Farmers found that many of these foxes had turned to raiding poultry because the foxes could not pursue and catch wild game while they were so weakened.

I believe these figures are low because a fox in an advanced state of mange is so repulsive to hunters that it is not submitted for bounty. Carcasses of such foxes should be burned or at least buried because the mange can spread to domestic animals.

Internally, the fox is infected by, or plays host to, helminths of various types and sizes. Among the trematodes are salmon-poisoning flukes which the fox ingests by eating raw fish that it picks up along the northwestern seacoast. This fluke affects the fox's small intestines; the lung fluke invades its lungs.

Two of the cestodes—*Echinococcus granulosa* and *Echinococcus multilocularis*—are of much greater importance because these hydatid tapeworms can on occasion be transmitted to man. Of the two, the latter is more deadly to man. It was established only in 1965 that *E. multilocularis* was present in foxes in the United States, although it had been reported in other parts of the world. Ordinarily the tapeworm

A red fox scratches a flea.

fastens itself with hooklets directly to the inner wall of the fox's small intestines, where it feeds.

To reproduce itself, the terminal segment of the tapeworm, which is full of fertilized eggs, breaks loose and is discharged from the fox's body in the feces. The eggs can be picked up by animals that eat grass and thus can reinfect the fox when the fox eats the grass-eating rodents or other animals. Or a dog can pick up the eggs on its coat and transmit them to a human who pets the dog or whom the dog licks with its tongue. Once the eggs are ingested by man, a hydatid cyst develops from each egg. Each of these cysts contains many tapeworm heads that can also reproduce even before the cyst is broken. The development of

89

these cysts in the human lungs, liver, brain, or bone marrow, to which they have traveled via the bloodstream, may cause enough pressure to cut off the flow of blood. If the cyst ruptures, releasing its fluid into the body, the human may go into shock because of an immunity response. However, we must realize that this degree of severity seldom occurs.

A fox is also plagued by a variety of nematodes or roundworms. The lungworms attack both the lungs and the bronchial tubes and can contribute to pneumonia. The heartworms and the kidney worms bore into those respective organs and may weaken them to the point where they fail. Hookworms in the small intestine can weaken a fox. Trichina (resulting in trichinosis), which a fox can pick up from eating pigs which have been thrown out on a refuse dump, can also affect man, but there is no direct link between man and the fox.

Two factors are of incalculable importance to the red fox: it is the least social member of the canine family in North America, and, except in breeding season, it does not use a den. Its isolationism prevents the direct transmission of parasites and diseases, so that the red fox is probably our healthiest canine.

Foxes are subject to a virus known as infectious encephalomyelitis. This virus affects the brain and nervous system of the fox. A fox having encephalomyelitis becomes lethargic, suffers paralysis and loss of motor control over first the hindquarters and then the front quarters, and finally goes into convulsions, with death following quickly. As the name implies, this virus is infectious to domestic animals, particularly dogs. However, it should not be confused with eastern equine encephalitis, the "sleeping sickness" that took twenty-one human lives in New Jersey in 1959. There is no known case of fox encephalitis's being transmitted to man.

Fox encephalomyelitis is much more prevalent among gray foxes than it is among red foxes because gray foxes are much more social than the red. Gray foxes use dens all year long, and these become focal points and repositories for viral infections. In 1962 there was a peak in gray fox encephalitis in New Jersey, and fox populations were decimated. Reports of "dopey" foxes and carcasses of the dead animals were numerous.

Although these parasites and viruses are health hazards to man, he fears rabies most. Rabies, sometimes referred to as hydrophobia, is an exceedingly deadly virus which an infected animal passes to a non-infected animal by biting it. In the process of biting, the virus which is present in the saliva of the infected animal enters the other animal's body and blood stream. There is usually an incubation period of several weeks to several months, during which time the virus makes its way, via the nervous system, to the newly infected animal's brain.

Creatures that are infected lose weight rapidly because they do not eat and have difficulty drinking. In advanced stages, the animals become violent and fearlessly attack anything with which they come into contact. If penned up at this stage, they frequently break their teeth biting at the bars or wires of their cages. Convulsions and paralysis are soon followed by death.

Outbreaks of rabies began to gain national recognition in the United States about 1941. Many kinds of animals have been infected. The dog is still the number one rabies vector, followed by the fox. Skunks, raccoons, opossums, wolves, coyotes, squirrels, rats, badgers, and weasels, as well as many other species, are affected. Even such diverse animals as cattle, deer, bats, and owls suffer from rabies. The Indiana Board of Health found rabies in only sixty-nine foxes in the period from 1947 to 1956. The foxes were only 1½ per cent of the total rabid creatures examined in that period.

When a rabies outbreak occurs in the wild, the most efficient method of control is a wide-scale reduction in the numbers of all the wild creatures and a mass rabies immunization of all dogs. It has been proved, however, that if all dogs were immunized in the first place, rabies could eventually be brought under complete control. Many countries, such as Great Britain, have obtained this control by inoculating all dogs.

As I write this, there are no serious outbreaks of rabies in the United States. In 1966, there were 4,197 cases of animal rabies. Skunks and foxes were involved in 57 per cent of the rabies cases for a total of 2,386. Skunks were number one with 1,522 cases, and foxes accounted for 864 cases. Bats figured in 377 cases, raccoons in 114, and the remaining 50 wildlife cases were among fourteen other species. One ten-year-old boy died of rabies in 1966 after being bitten by a striped skunk.

To prevent a needless loss of human lives, livestock, and wild creatures, I feel that the Federal Government should make it mandatory for all dogs to be immunized against rabies.

Autumn

AUTUMN is the most beautiful time of the year. Spring and summer each have their individual color and charm, but they are only dress rehearsals for Nature's greatest creative production. In autumn the sky is bluer, the air is crisp and lighter, the colors brighter. The days are warm, but the nights are cool. Gone is the somnolent lethargy of summer; fulfilled is the promise of the flowering spring. It is harvest time, and most of the creatures, in a frenzy of activity, are participating in the sumptuous bounty provided by a benevolent Creator.

Chipmunks scurry back and forth to their burrows, making an exhausting number of trips each day. Their bulging cheek pouches make them appear to have mumps. The deer and the squirrels compete for the fallen nut crop. The deer gorge themselves on acorns, preferring the white acorns to all other foods. Squirrels bury their share of the nuts either singly or in caches, heeding an intuitive urge to provide for the long winter ahead. The beaver are busy anchoring hundreds of tree branches in the mud at the bottom of the pond near their lodges, to be utilized when the pond's frozen surface cuts off their access to the forest world. Woodchucks, marmots, and ground squirrels have stored the sun's energy, which they ingested from the grasses they ate, in layers of fat on their bodies. This energy will keep the spark of life flickering throughout the long winter months that will be spent in hibernation. The bears, raccoons, skunks, and opossums have stuffed themselves, too, with everything edible to insulate their bodies against

93

the rigors and wants of the forthcoming winter. Although none of these four animals are true hibernators, the stored fat will allow them to remain inactive for extended periods of time. The opossum has hairless ears, feet, and tail, not adapted to extremely cold weather; it also has the misfortune of being unable to remain in its winter den as long as the other three animals.

The predators neither sow nor do they reap. They cannot hibernate; they do not migrate; they do not store food for the future. Their way of life means that they must be active every day of the year, despite inclement weather or freezing cold, in a constant search for food. They are all opportunists and avail themselves of whatever food they are able to get.

The nature and habits of the predators vary according to the species. The polar bear is strictly carnivorous and is such an efficient hunter that it seldom returns to its prey. If it kills a seal, it gorges itself on the blubber and then retires to sleep, leaving the meat on the carcass to the arctic foxes, the most provident of the scavenging predators, and also the only predators to have caches of food laid by in the summer for winter use.

The black bears and the grizzly and big brown bears are not efficient hunters and have slowly evolved into omnivorous creatures whose main diet is vegetation. This transition can easily be verified by noting their flat-topped grinding molars. When these bears kill or find a dead animal, they remain near the carcass until everything edible is consumed. Bears guarding such carcasses are extremely dangerous.

The cats of North America, from the large cougar to the small bobcat, all have the same habit of eating what they can of a kill and then covering the remainder with debris to hide it from sight. They return and eat from the carcass only as long as the meat stays fresh. Once it becomes tainted, the cats abandon the meat.

Wolves are very efficient killers and can usually secure food whenever they need it. This shows up in their habit of eating all they can hold when they make a kill and then often abandoning the remainder. It is rare for a wolf to return to a kill unless the hunting is very poor and the wolf is forced to.

Coyotes, gray foxes, and red foxes more frequently cache food by burying it than does the wolf. This caching is temporary, however, and is not the result of long-range planning. These animals will bury surplus game if it is more than they can eat at one time or if the game is caught after the animals have filled their bellies.

A red fox can consume about one pound of meat per day, although it is often forced to get by on much less. Adult meadow voles weigh about two ounces apiece, and Elton Clark killed one red fox that had eight of them in its stomach. A full-grown cottontail rabbit weighs a little over two pounds and therefore provides enough food to last the fox for two days.

When a red fox kills a rabbit, it usually eats part of the organs, such as the heart, liver, lungs, and the forequarters, first. The hindquarters, being tougher and stringier, are less desirable, and that part is cached.

The selection of a cache appears random, although the fox may have some purpose, unknown to us, for choosing the site. Using its front feet, the fox quickly digs a small hole into which it drops its prey. The fox then uses its nose to tamp the prey into the hole and to cover it up. The feet are used for digging the hole, but only the nose is used to finish the job. These caches are not dug deep, and I have never seen more than 1 to 2 inches of dirt over the prey. They are comparatively easy to find because the excess dirt that has been dug out is usually spread fanwise back from the holes.

As a miser, so the stories go, gets great pleasure out of running his fingers through his gold, the red fox gets great pleasure out of visiting its caches. Whenever the fox is in the vicinity of one of its caches, it goes to it, digs it up, and as often as not simply reburies it in the same spot. Or it may carry it off a short distance and then rebury it. It is just as if the fox wanted to reassure itself that all was well with its stores.

A red fox digs a cache hole.

A ground squirrel lies in front of the hole, ready to be cached.

The fox covers the cache with its nose.

In the winter when the earth is frozen, the fox caches its prey under dead leaves and debris and also buries it under snow.

During the winter of 1934, a study of cottontail rabbits was made on the Edwin S. George Reserve near Pinckney, Michigan. The study proved that the cottontail population was exceptionally high and that the red foxes were taking advantage of the situation. The trail of a pair of red foxes in the snow led to the discovery of seven cottontails killed in a single night. Most of the kills had been made by the larger male red fox. None of the rabbits had been eaten, which proved that the foxes had evidently fed before the trails of the cottontails were discovered and followed. Six of the rabbits had been cached under the snow, while the seventh was left lying exposed on the top. These cached rabbits were checked daily, and it was seen that the foxes had returned and eaten some of them. The tracks also showed that the foxes had moved the uneaten cached rabbits several times and that skunks, hawks, owls, and crows had fed on some of the rabbits that the melting snows had revealed. Foxes themselves may feed on another fox's cache.

By late August the red fox family has split up, even the adult male and female going their separate ways. The same adults may get together again in the winter prior to the breeding season, but during autumn the red fox reverts to its true character of being a loner.

A red fox's winter range is larger than its summer range because food is scarcer in the winter. As a general rule, a fox can range over ten square miles, but I have found that they usually stay within about 1,000 acres. During the many times that I have followed fox trails, I have noted that most of their travels are contained within five to ten fields of about ten acres each, although in their hunting they travel about five miles nightly.

The breakup of the family unit is the period of dispersal for the pups. It is at this time that some of the foxes travel their greatest distance, although most of them remain in the general area. The male

The remains of a rabbit eaten by a fox lie in the snow.

pups usually disperse first and travel the greatest distance.

The two extremes of this are well illustrated by two male red fox pups that were live-snared and tagged with metal collars on August 29, 1962, in the University of Wisconsin Arboretum and Wildlife Refuge at Madison, Wisconsin. One of these foxes set the long-distance record when it was shot by a woodchuck hunter on May 20, 1963, in Montgomery County, Indiana, which is 245 miles south-southeast in a straight line from Madison. The second fox was resnared on June 17, 1963, just 300 yards from the original tagging point.

In late summer the young red fox is ready to travel alone.

William Sheldon found that one red fox male that was tagged during the dispersal period traveled 23 miles in eleven days. Another tagged at the same time was trapped in early December and had traveled 40 miles.

One red female was an exception to the general rule that the females stay near their birth area. This animal was tagged at the Mud Lake National Waterfowl Refuge near Holt, Minnesota, on June 4, 1959. She was retrapped on April 10, 1961, at Elm Creek, Manitoba, Canada, a distance of 126 miles. A male red fox tagged at Mud Lake on September 12, 1959, was found dead on April 7, 1960, only ½ mile from where it had been tagged. Perhaps more females travel farther than we suspect, but our information is scanty because of the difficulty in live-trapping and tagging any fox. More males are trapped because they travel about more.

Nelson Swink tagged a red female on April 30, 1951, at Blacksburg, Virginia. This fox was found drowned in a muskrat trap on February 7, 1952, in Russell County, Virginia, a distance of 110 air miles.

Errington and Berry in 1937 reported one red male pup tagged in Iowa that had moved 160 miles. Two red males in another litter, tagged in June at the Rose Lake Wildlife Experiment Station in Michigan, had been killed by early winter. One had traveled 73 miles to Clare, Michigan, and the second had traveled 166 miles to Leelanau County, Michigan.

Red foxes are expanding their range in all directions at the present time. It is suspected that the red fox may now be in the western tip of the Floridian panhandle. Florida is the only one of the forty-nine continental states in which the red fox has not been found. The arctic invasion by red foxes began in 1918 when this species first crossed the ice of Hudson Strait to Baffin Island. By 1962 the foxes had pushed 750 miles farther north and had crossed Lancaster Sound to Devon Island, where two were caught at Resolute Bay and one at Grise Fiord, both situated at a latitude of about 72 degrees. This is the northernmost recorded latitude at which the red fox has been found on the North American continent.

The foxes that do not have to move out of the area where they were born have the greatest chance of survival, possibly because the terrain is familiar to them. They know what represents danger and what does not. They know where to expect to find food. As the pups grow larger and travel farther from their den, this knowledge of their surroundings is gradually increased, and even though they move a mile or two away the traveling is not a hardship.

If a fox pup lives long enough, it gets to know its new range intimately. The longer it lives, the greater are its chances of survival because of this knowledge.

Red foxes prefer to travel in open country. They walk along the edges of woods, along the fencerows surrounding a field, along horse paths, cattle trails, and old wood roads, and even run on steel railroad rails. They know where high water has spilled sand and gravel over the lowlands, creating an open path through the rank vegetation. They know where every gate, barway, or opening is in every fence. They know where every brook or stream can be crossed on the rocks or on a fallen tree. They walk in the last open furrow in any plowed field. They know their range as intimately as if their life depended on it, which it does.

Radios attached to live foxes have provided greater knowledge of foxes' activities at night than has any other method. They have proved that a red fox returns to the same general area each morning to sleep through the day, although it does not use the same bed. Radio tracking has shown what snow tracking had already established—that a fox is seldom still all night long. Neither temperature, cloud cover, moonlight, nor precipitation stays the fox from its self-appointed rounds.

In autumn the pups attain their winter coat of fur before the adults do. The adults are always several weeks to a month later. By the latter part of October or the first of November, all the red foxes are resplen-

The red fox is protected from the winter winds and snow by a dense fur coat.

dent in their new winter coats. At eight to nine months of age the pups are almost indistinguishable from the adults, although they weigh less.

It is during the autumn that most of the red foxes attain their maximum weight. The weather is cool enough to stimulate both their activities and their appetites, and food is still plentiful.

Wild fruits, particularly wild cherries, are especially important to red foxes in September. Every fox in every area eats all the little dark cherries it can pick up. As the fruit acts as a laxative, fox voidings are very much in evidence. In fact, the droppings become so plentiful and are so conspicuous that many people are misled as to the actual number of foxes in an area. They do not realize that the more an animal eats, the more it voids without getting more nutrients out of the food. Many of the berries pass through the fox in their entirety. Meat that is consumed is utilized to a greater degree and stays in the body for a longer period of time; hence meat voidings are far scarcer per fox than are berry voidings.

Note the hair of a prey animal in these scats, or droppings, of the red fox.

Wild grapes are also eaten by foxes as are the last of the blueberries. Every fox knows the place where every orchard or wild apple tree stands, and it always visits all of these on its rounds. Apples, because they are so common, are a very important fox food. Persimmons that are sweetened and fall after a frost are added to the fox's diet.

Deer and squirrels are not the only creatures to enjoy the bonanza of fallen nuts. The red fox eats beechnuts and acorns and sometimes even the heavier shelled hickory nuts. In the Southern states foxes eat pecans. The walnuts' thick shells are too much of a task for a fox and are not utilized.

During September and early October insects such as crickets and grasshoppers have reached their peak in numbers and size. In fall these

Grasshoppers are important as red fox food in late summer.

insects are easier to catch because the cool nights render them quite helpless, and the torpid insects are eaten in large numbers by the foxes. Now is the only time of year when the fox can dig out the nests of the yellow jackets with impunity.

Mice at this season are exceedingly plentiful, easily caught, and provide the fox with the bulk of its meat diet. The red fox has a decided preference for the meadow vole over the white-footed mouse. Meadow voles, much more plentiful than are the white-foots, are found in the more open areas where the red fox prefers to hunt, but the white-footed mouse is more alert and usually inhabits a brushy area which offers more avenues of escape when needed. The preference of the fox for the meadow vole over the white-footed mouse is supported by the fact that the fox caches the white-foot but eats the vole at once. Meadow voles are very destructive, and it has been figured that as few as 100 mice to an acre of hay will destroy 4 per cent of the crop.

Cottontail rabbits and jack rabbits are also caught more frequently in fall than during the summer. In many areas rabbit-hunting by foxes increases as ground squirrels, chipmunks, woodchucks, and marmots go into hibernation.

Red foxes at all times kill every mole, shrew, or snake that they can find and catch, but they seldom eat any of them. Such prey is killed and then left lying on the ground.

103

In most of the states the waterfowl and small-game hunting seasons open in October and November. Far too many hunters attempt to kill game at too long a range, and many don't use dogs to retrieve the birds that they have crippled. Although this crippled game is often lost to the hunters, it does help feed the predators. The predators find it so much easier to catch the cripples and to scavenge the game found dead that they inadvertently reduce their pressure on the other living game species.

Foxes not only feed on ducks crippled by hunters, but also hunt for ducks themselves. A unique but common method used by foxes to catch ducks is known as "tolling." When a fox is trying to toll the ducks in to shore, it picks up a stick and prances and jumps about on the beach, playing in plain sight of the ducks. The ducks, curious about such antics, swim in closer to get a better look. The fox pays no attention to the ducks but concentrates on its playing, although now it has moved back a bit from the shore. The ducks swim in closer, and still the fox seems oblivious to their presence. Finally, as if tiring of the play, the fox disappears from the ducks' view by hiding behind some reeds or bushes. The ducks that are foolish enough to waddle out on land to follow the fox suddenly find that it is in their midst and has soon captured at least one of them. So successful is this method that for many years a special mixed breed of medium-sized yellow dogs has been trained to toll in ducks close enough to shore that hunters can get a shot at them. Whatever the ancestry of the dogs may have been, only the yellow dogs are used because only they look like red foxes. Duck tolling was at one time very popular along the entire New England coast, but it is now mainly used in Nova Scotia. Black ducks, scaups, redheads, and buffleheads are the species most easily tolled.

Red foxes also catch ducks that are feeding along or resting on the shores of lakes, rivers, and ponds. Bradley Bowen, while duck hunting on the Horicon Marsh in Wisconsin, shot a red fox that was stalking his decoys. A Mr. Calwell, of Widnoon, Pennsylvania, also had an odd experience with a red fox. He shot a gray squirrel that was snatched up by a red fox as soon as it hit the ground. Mr. Calwell got both the fox and the squirrel.

The red foxes have different hunting techniques that are used in hunting different kinds of game. While following the foxes on their hunting rounds in Alaska, I found that I was able to tell what kind of game the foxes were hunting by their actions.

The foxes usually hunted upwind so that the scent of their prey would be wafted down to them. Sometimes they coursed back and forth; at other times they worked upwind, following whatever paths or trails were in the area. They usually hunted by scent and sound because they held their heads and tails low. When game was either scented or heard, the heads came up in an attempt to see the prey.

In marshes, red foxes sometimes feed on mallard ducks or eat eggs from their nests.

A red fox stalks its prey.

Songbirds and game birds, which are always very alert, are carefully stalked. The fox drops down so that its belly almost touches the ground. Its shoulder blades and sometimes its elbows are hunched above the back, the head is held straight out in front, and the ears are cocked forward. Keeping behind every bit of cover, the fox carefully works its way as close as possible. If it can get within 12 to 15 feet, its rushing attack is so fast that it can usually catch the bird before the bird can take off. Rabbits are stalked in the same manner, although many times, after starting the rabbit, the fox must run it down in open pursuit. Ground squirrels, woodchucks, and marmots are usually hunted by sight, or the fox moves in on their whistling chirps. The fox usually waits until the ground dweller goes down into its burrow. As soon as it is out of sight, the fox dashes up and conceals itself behind any piece of cover that is available. When the squirrel or marmot comes out again to feed, the fox rushes out and grabs it before it can return to the safety of its burrow.

Mice and voles are usually hunted by sound and not stalked. As voles are often hidden from the sight of the fox by high grass, the fox is also hidden from the voles. When the fox hears a mouse or a vole, it runs to the area and pounces on any movement that it can detect in the grass. If there is no movement, the fox stands up on its hind legs, pirouetting like a dancer, ready to pounce at the first telltale movement of its prey. Naturalists and hunters have found that they can imitate the squeal of a mouse by kissing the back of one hand, and can often call a fox in close with this ruse.

Red foxes often stand upright.

Quite frequently in both spring and fall, hard, prolonged rains cause rivers and streams to overflow their banks. Such flooding forces every mouse and vole out of its runways and burrows, and the fox is quick to take advantage of the situation.

In the eastern part of the United States the foxes have real hunting competition from feral house cats. Thousands upon thousands of these cats roam the woods, where they have been abandoned by thoughtless humans. A cat is a perfect killing machine and an even better stalker than the fox. Although the fox appears much larger because of its long fur, many of these cats weigh as much as a fox. The fox is one of the few controls on the number of these animals because most red foxes will kill every cat they encounter.

I know of several people who have watched foxes chase their cats out of fields and run them up on the home porches. There is also a report of a cat that was too tough for a fox. Henry Urich, of Newport, Pennsylvania, shot a red fox that his cat had backed into a fence corner.

During the autumn many bow hunters often get shots at foxes. To do so, most of them wear camouflage clothing which blends with their surroundings. Almost all bow hunting is done from a blind or a tree stand, so the fox has no idea that a hunter is in the woods until the bow twangs.

However, it is not the bow hunter that the fox has to fear at this time, but the trapper. Most fox trapping is done before the ground freezes or the first snow falls. Fox trappers are well aware of the fact that a fox caches some of its surplus food, and they are also aware that a fox takes cached food of other foxes. So the most popular and deadly trap set is known as the "dirt hole set" in which a trap is buried beneath loose dirt in front of a small hole made to look exactly like the cache that a fox makes. Odorous bait is used to attract the fox to the trap. More foxes are caught with this method than with any other.

Most of the foxes that are trapped are young ones because numerically they outnumber the adults—about 73 per cent young to 27 per cent adults. The adult foxes are those that have survived from previous years. They are much more aware of the dangers of their environment and have probably had some experience with traps. Another factor in the trapper's favor is that he is trapping during the dispersal time of the young foxes, which may not know the area they are in and have only recently had to provide for themselves. The trapper's tempting bait then becomes irresistible. More males than females are caught because the males travel more.

In addition to the "dirt hole set," trappers make "blind sets" in which a trap is concealed beneath the dirt in a path or runway that they know foxes will frequent. Often a fox becomes suspicious of a large bait such as a dead chicken. In order to see better without going too close, the fox may jump up on a stump or high anthill mound. Trappers knowing of this habit set traps in just such places and provide a bait large enough to make the fox suspicious. When the ground freezes and the trap can no longer be hidden beneath the dirt, trappers make water sets. Spring water does not freeze because it comes out of the earth warmer than the surrounding temperature. Trappers make two tiny islands out from shore. The first island near the shore conceals the trap, and the bait is on the second island. In attempting to get at the bait, the fox is forced to step into the trap.*

When snow comes, trapping can be carried on only where the temperature is cold enough to prevent the snow from melting during the daytime and freezing during the night. Traps are placed under a fox's tracks in the snow because a trapper knows that every fox in the area will walk through deep snow by placing its feet exactly in the tracks of

---

Editor's Note: The use of steel-jawed traps to catch foxes and other fur-bearing animals is considered callous and uncivilized by many conservationists, naturalists, and humane societies. They recommend the use of live traps, which usually capture the animals unharmed, or any other methods that spare the animals pain or extended suffering.

its predecessor. Or a trap may be placed directly on top of a bait and everything covered with snow and smoothed over. In digging down to get the bait, the fox may be caught.

In the Far North snares are used to catch foxes by the neck as they travel along their paths. Snares are not used in rural areas because they kill whatever animal they catch, and the snare can't tell the difference between a fox and a dog.

Fox trapping is a science, and the successful trapper does not divulge his secrets. Most of the time he couldn't tell his secrets if he wanted to. Many of them are intuitive; from years of studying the fox and its habits, the trapper knows where the foxes are most likely to be, where they are likely to travel, what they will be eating, etc.

Both New York State and Michigan have done extensive work on foxes. Most of the records of live-trapped foxes that are available come from those two states. One point is of tremendous importance: the records show that there is an exceptionally high annual mortality rate. Averaging the records of all the foxes that had been live-trapped, tagged and released, and retaken proved this. In New York the foxes lived an average of 178 days after being tagged; in Michigan they survived for an average of 187 days.

Winter

THE SNOW began in midmorning. There was no dawn, just a lessening of the total darkness of night. The sky was filled with a dark batting of clouds. Months before, most of the migratory birds had abandoned the now bleak fields and woodlands for the more available food and moderate climate of the southern regions. The snowbirds and even the effervescent wintering chickadees now huddled in the thickets and fluffed out their feathers, waiting expectantly. Most of the mammals had retired to their burrows, to their forms, or into dense cover. Not a creature stirred.

The snowflakes sifted down slowly at first, then cascaded down when the feather ticking of the sky had been rent asunder. Gradually the harsh realities of the landscape were softened, remolded by the mantle of new snow.

The snow puzzled the young red fox; never had it experienced the fluffy stuff. Curled up in the middle of a stubble field, the fox felt an inner restlessness which pushed back the feelings of sleep that a night's traveling and a full stomach had prompted. The first flakes momentarily lingered on the fox's long fur, and a cold sensation was all that remained when the fox examined the flakes with its warm tongue. As the ground began to lose its identity, the fox arose and tentatively stepped out of its bare bed. Immediately it retreated back to its bed, turned around a few times, and resettled itself into a ball. Placing its tail over its feet and its head, the fox slowly drifted into sleep. At the same time the snow began to drift over the fox, gradually masking its identity, creating one more white mound in an already white expanse.

The snow offers many things to many creatures. To the dormant plant life, the snow's protective blanket provides the insulation which prevents their freezing. To the smaller mammals such as the shrews, voles, and mice, the snow's opaqueness screens their activities from the eyes of the predators and allows them freedom of movement such as they experience at no other time of year. In a very short time these

The season's first snow covers a red fox's coat.

A red fox searches for mice in the snow.

creatures have a network of trails, paths, and byways laid out, down which they scurry to carry on their activities. To many of the larger creatures the snow forecloses the mortgage on easy living. With the snow masking most of what little food is left, the period of want, hunger, and hardship is ushered in.

When the young fox arose in the early evening, it shook the snow from its coat and started off to hunt. The hairs between its toes had increased in length steadily throughout autumn as the hours of day-

113

light had decreased. By now its toe pads were almost obscured, so that the fox did not mind the cold or walking in the snow. However, the snow's depth did make walking harder, requiring more calories to be consumed by the fox's internal furnace. They were calories that would become increasingly hard to replace. Many times the fox stopped throughout the night to thrust its nose down through the snow in an attempt to catch the voles and mice whose body odors it could detect even through the crystals. Each time its jaws closed on nothing but snow. Although its mouth was filled, its belly was not. As the snow was still drifting down, the rabbits had not moved, each huddling snug in its form or in the entrance of a woodchuck's burrow. When the snow stopped, the rabbits would move, but not before. As dawn began to lighten the eastern horizon, the fox scoured an old orchard and was rewarded to find one frozen, shriveled apple that had been overlooked by the deer only because they were seeking shelter in the coniferous swamps.

During the winter, foxes are on an almost straight meat diet for the reason that animal life is all that is generally available. Orchards are visited constantly for the few frozen apples that hang on the bare limbs of the trees throughout the winter. One by one these drop off and are usually taken by foxes because deer seldom bother to come to the orchards after the first snows. Occasionally a red fox feeds on an ear of field corn that has escaped the notice of both the squirrels and the deer. In wilderness areas the fox is on a 100 per cent meat diet.

The error for the uninitiated in attempting to judge an animal's food habits from remnants that show up in its voidings becomes apparent in December. Deer hair, for example, is frequently found in the red fox's scats throughout the winter. It is not that the fox is killing deer (there is only one record of a red fox's actually doing so), but it is proof that the fox is an efficient scavenger. Deer hunters provide the fox with the greatest reprieve from hunger that they will experience until spring is well under way. That such losses, through illegal hunt-

Deer that die of starvation are a main source of food for the red fox in winter.

ing or crippling, run into thousands upon thousands of deer can easily be seen by the results of some of the extensive surveys made by various state game departments. Some deer losses through crippling are unavoidable, but others are the direct results of unsportsmanlike behavior on the part of some hunters, fostered by the "bucks only" law erroneously adhered to by a number of states.

The Wisconsin State Department of Conservation has shown that when an "any deer" season (permitting both bucks and does can be shot) is allowed, illegal kills are minimal. During the "bucks only" season there are some hunters who shoot at any deer, hoping that the one they kill will be a legal buck. When the slain deer turns out to be a doe, the hunter quickly vacates the area and leaves the deer lying in the woods.

Accurate surveys made in various deer-hunting areas have shown that the percentage of illegal kills, from counted carcasses, to the percentage of known declared legal kills has varied from 60 to 500 illegal deer kills per 100 legal deer kills. The highest ratio of illegal kills is always on lands that are open to the general public during a "bucks only" season. I know from personal experience that even on club, or restricted, lands, the illegal deer kill is excessive and inexcusable.

While this works a hardship for deer, it is a bonanza for the predators, which soon locate every carcass, leaving little to go to waste. In addition to the deer-hunting losses, tens of thousands of deer die of starvation each winter. Many people wonder how it can be told whether the deer died of starvation or was an illegal kill when all that remains in the spring is a bleached carcass. If the marrow in a deer's hind leg bone is red, it is sure proof that the deer died of starvation, and this simple test can be conducted by anyone in the field.*

When a hunter kills a legal deer, he immediately eviscerates the animal on the spot. The predators will visit these remains, too, until everything edible is gone. It is so well known that foxes feed on such carcasses that some state biologists, when running deer surveys, follow all the fox tracks, which eventually lead to every deer carcass in the woods.

Foxes feed on almost any carcass they can find. In 1955, in Stutsman County, North Dakota, two biologists flying in a light plane noticed a red fox traveling toward a sheep carcass. The fox encountered trouble at the carcass because a badger had reached there first and had no intention of sharing its prize. Approaching the carcass, the fox soon displayed both its superior intelligence and speed. It harassed the badger into chasing it, but when the badger was about 150 feet from the carcass, the fox doubled back and bit off some before the badger could return. While the biologists circled overhead, the fox used this ploy five or six times.

As other predators often feed on fox caches, so the fox feeds on the remains of prey killed by other predators. The red fox feeds on wolf kills, and in the Far North it has also been seen following a wolverine in the hope of scavenging from one of its kills.

In scavenging, the foxes often take things that are of little value to them. The red fox has a penchant for chewing on the dried feet of any dead duck it can find. It will also chew on turkey and chicken feet, but a duck's foot is the pièce de résistance. I have seen a number of rubber

Editor's Note: Mr. Rue thoroughly discussed the problems of deer in his book, *The World of the White-tailed Deer,* the first volume in our Living World series.

teat cups discarded from cow-milking machines that have been picked up, carried, and chewed by a fox. Evidently enough of the odor of the cow and the milk remained in the cup to convince it that they were edible.

At the Coventry Hunting Club in New Jersey, we sometimes have a high mortality among pheasants from great horned owls. I have found as many as five or six pheasants killed in a single night by these big birds. The owl-kill can easily be identified because only the head, the neck, part of the back, and the crop have been eaten. The remaining carcass provides a couple of good meals for the fox if it finds it before the crows pick it clean.

The red fox also hunts the pheasant but does the species little harm. In Michigan, biologists followed red fox tracks in the snow for about 1,000 miles in an effort to gain a better understanding of this predator. In 577 measured miles, the investigators came upon only three pheasants that had been killed by foxes. Surveys carried out in the spring showed that there were seventy-five pheasants and one fox to a square

Red foxes sometimes prey on ruffed grouse.

These ruffed grouse eggs were eaten by a red fox.

mile. The biologists came to the conclusion that each fox probably killed four pheasants per winter for a total of less than 2 per cent of the pheasant population.

The fox is not much more dangerous to quail. These birds usually frequent such dense cover that the fox has great difficulty in approaching them undetected. At night the quail sleep in a tight circle, their bodies touching, their tails to the center and their heads out. Thus the quail cover 360 degrees to watch for danger. As one or two of the birds in the covey are almost always awake at any given time, the fox is usually detected in time for the birds to escape.

In the spring, the fox may at times have more of an influence on the ruffed grouse than any other predator because it is so successful in finding the nests and eating the eggs.* In winter, the great horned owl

Editor's Note: Dr. Ralph T. King, in his Minnesota studies of ruffed grouse, found an interesting correlation between foxes, grouse, and chipmunks. Chipmunks sometimes develop the playful habit of rolling grouse eggs out of the nest. The female grouse does not retrieve them, and the eggs go unhatched. Foxes prey considerably on chipmunks and inadvertently eliminate many chipmunks as potential threats to grouse eggs. Some of our highest populations of grouse and other game species live side by side with high predator populations if the environment for the game species is favorable or "secure."

preys on grouse, and what little remains after the bird has eaten is often scavenged by the fox. During extremely cold weather the grouse sometimes plunges into soft snowbanks and buries itself beneath the surface. The insulation of the snow protects the bird from the inclement weather, but it also masks the approach of the fox, which occasionally is able to catch the grouse before it can break free from the drift and fly away.

Foxes can catch mice beneath 4 to 5 inches of snow. When the snow is deeper than that, the meadow voles are fairly secure in their hidden runways. The white-footed mice scamper across the top of the snow and are more frequently caught at this time, although the voles are greatly preferred by the fox. As the snow deepens, hiding such buffer species as the voles, the fox preys more heavily on the more available rabbits and hares.

Both the varying hare and the white-tailed jack rabbit turn white in winter, and their protective coloration helps them escape foxes almost as much as does their swiftness of foot. In soft, deep snow both of these

White-footed mice are an important winter food for the red fox.

A cottontail rabbit, prey of foxes, runs for its life.

In the north the red fox feeds on varying hares.

hares, because of their large, furry feet which buoy them as snowshoes hold up a man, have a great advantage over the fox. When the snow settles, however, and becomes crusted or packed in the hares' trails, the contest is more even and the fox has a chance of catching a hare.

In the arctic the red foxes abandon the open land because of the cold and the piercing wind and seek out the willow-lined gullies and draws. Not only does the fox get some protection there from the elements, but it gathers most of its food in such places. The lemmings are under the snow, but the arctic hares and the ptarmigans, in white coats that help prevent their detection by predators, are on top of the snow feeding on seeds or other parts of plants.

Although woodchucks are a favored fox food, apparently the fox does little feeding on them when they are below ground in their winter sleep. When a woodchuck is ready to hibernate in its burrow, it digs out a side passageway or tunnel to be used as its sleeping chamber. Before dropping off into its torpor, the woodchuck seals the chamber from the main tunnel with dirt. Evidently the fox cannot locate the woodchuck because its remains do not show up in the fox's winter droppings. All woodchucks would soon be eaten if they could be found because in their lethargic state they could offer no resistance to predation.

In the winter the red fox preys on the opossum because it is available. At other times of year the opossum is seldom taken for food.

The ice that covers ponds and rivers forces muskrats to feed beneath the surface. The ice prevents their being eaten by the foxes because it limits muskrat excursions on land where they are vulnerable to predatory animals.

In times of need, some red foxes have been known to kill and eat porcupines. In attacking the animal, the fox keeps circling the porcupine, causing it to turn, too. When the opportunity presents itself, the fox seizes the porcupine by the nose and backs up, pulling its victim after it. When the porcupine is stretched out, the fox flips it over on its back and quickly bites its chest, crushing the heart and killing it. That many foxes cannot do this is seen by the number of red foxes that have been killed or found dead with their faces full of porcupine quills.

The mainstay of the red fox in winter is the cottontail rabbit. It provides as much as 60 per cent or even more of the fox's winter diet. Given the proper habitat, the rabbit population can easily withstand the combined pressure of all the predators and survive. The proof of this statement is that cottontails have been surviving foxes and other predators for millions of years.

The State of Pennsylvania figures that it loses about 5,000,000 cottontails between September first and November first. Many of these are eaten by foxes before the hunters even get a shot at them. After the hunting season the population has been thinned, but cottontails are still subject to tremendous predation throughout the winter. Records from live-trapping, tagging, and impounded areas have shown that 85 per cent of the entire cottontail population dies or is killed every year whether hunted or not. What is even more remarkable is that almost the same percentage died even when the rabbits were protected from predation. The foxes are excellent hunters, coursing far and wide in their search for rabbits, checking every bit of available cover, but they do not control the number of cottontails and they never have.

At any time of year the red fox may be abroad in the daytime, killing and eating such prey as squirrels, chipmunks, woodchucks, and other rodents. In winter, however, when food is scarce, such sightings are more common because the fox has to hunt longer and because more hunters are out at that time of year hunting foxes.

Fox hunting is an old and honorable sport and has tens of thousands of advocates in the United States. All of them agree that the red fox is the finest game animal, the smartest and the trickiest, but that is all they do agree on. Foxes are hunted in many ways by many people in various sections of the country. Hunting methods that are common in one area are disapproved of in another. Foxes are hunted from stands, on foot, on horseback, or from machines. In some sections of the country the goal of the hunt is to kill the fox; in other sections the hunt is more important than the quarry. Regardless of the outcome of the hunt, one thing is certain: it brings out the best in the fox, giving it a chance to live up to its reputation for intelligence. Each hunt usually adds just a bit more to its revered status of being a clever, sagacious animal.

One of the most difficult methods of fox hunting is silent trailing, or "still hunting." The man who can walk up on a fox has to be in good physical condition and must have a lot of know-how about his quarry. Such fox tracking is usually done right after a fresh fall of snow. The hunter either goes to an area that he knows is frequented by foxes or else drives down back roads until he finds a fox track. The hunter then follows the tracks in the hope of jumping the fox out of its bed and getting a shot at it before the fox is out of range.

Foxes usually sleep in open fields if they are not molested. If they have been hunted steadily or if the wind is blowing hard, they lie in a sheltered area. Foxes detest the wind, which blows their fur aside and penetrates to the skin. Many hunters believe that a fox always lies on the sunny side of a hill. It usually does unless the wind is blowing there, whereupon shelter from the wind may be preferable. If possible, the fox seeks out an elevation, no matter how slight, as a bedding area so that it can watch for approaching danger. In the absolutely flat farm lands of Ohio, Indiana, and Illinois, the fox often sleeps on a mound of hay or straw.

Working with foxes in Alaska, I found that when they sleep in the open they usually doze for fifteen to twenty-five seconds and then wake up, look around carefully, and nap again. At such times their breathing is light and shallow. Only when the fox sleeps in dense cover does it go into a heavy sleep, which can be recognized by the deep, slow breathing and the fact that the fox's ears relax. In dense cover the fox

Red foxes sleep out in the snow all winter.

depends on the sound of anything approaching to awaken it. In such a sleep the fox may not stir itself to look around for an hour or more at a time.

The still hunter knows that when a fox track weaves all over an area, the fox is hunting; when the track straightens out, the fox is usually traveling to its bedding area; and when the tracks start to circle, it means that the fox is probably bedded nearby. Most often the hunter then walks well off to one side of the track, taking care not to make any noise and to keep the wind in his favor.

124

Winter

No matter how much care the hunter takes, the fox usually bolts out of its bed before he can locate it. Most of the time the hunter sees nothing but a few red hairs frozen into the fox's bed and a set of new tracks leading off into the distance.

A novice hunter may start out in immediate pursuit, but this is what the fox expects. The experienced hunter sits down and waits after jumping the fox, and perhaps he eats his lunch. When the fox discovers it is not being followed, it soon beds down again. This continues until the hunter shoots the fox or it leaves the area. A fox that is frightened from its bed after 3:30 P.M. will probably keep on moving about and start its evening hunt early. By 4:00 P.M., most still hunters head back for their cars or homes, either of which may now be many miles away. Still hunting is probably the most challenging form of fox hunting, pitting the man's knowledge against the animal's superior senses.

A red fox trots through the snow. Note how the wind has blown the fox's fur aside.

Sometimes three hunters work together, forming a wide V. The hunter following the tracks is at the apex of the V; the other two hunters are ahead of him, perhaps 400 feet apart. Thus, when the tracking hunter starts the fox, one or the other of the outlying hunters may get a shot.

A variation of this method is known as "belling." The hunters move forward in the same way, except that the tracking hunter carries, instead of a gun, a large cow bell, which he clangs every few steps as he walks along. The fox hears the cow bell but usually doesn't associate it with danger. Perhaps the fox is curious about the source of the sound —in any event its attention is focused on the bell and this may allow the outside hunters to get close enough to it for a shot.

In the Midwestern states hunting clubs sometimes hold gang hunts. The action varies according to how many men participate. If perhaps a dozen of them join together, the hunt is like a deer drive; eight of the men station themselves around the perimeter of the area to be hunted while four go in to drive the fox out. Sometimes, if the area is small enough, the hunters station themselves uniformly apart. If the area is larger, they try to anticipate the actual crossing that will be used by the fox.

On some of these drives as many as 200 hunters participate. As most of the areas are laid out in squares, the men line up all along the surrounding road. At a given signal they all walk toward the center of the square as the hunters try to push the fox in ahead of them. Foxes, naturally uncooperative in such matters, will frequently sneak back through the advancing lines to escape.

Predator calling is becoming very popular, and in areas where the fox is not hunted heavily, it is successful in luring the animal. Calling foxes goes back a long way in history. The Indians were able to call foxes by squealing like a mouse. About twenty to twenty-five years ago, fox calls were put on the market that, when blown, sounded like a dying rabbit. These calls, made out of metal, wood, and plastic, all work on the same principle: Air blown through the tube and forced over a thin reed imitates the squeal of an injured rabbit. Most predators are always interested in a sick or injured animal, and most of them respond in the hope of catching it. Living as we do in an electronic age, it was only a short time before someone made records of this call and sold them with a portable phonograph and amplifier. Now more efficient tapes are being used, and the units have been made smaller and more compact. Murry and Winston Burnham, of Marble Falls, Texas, are perhaps the most successful predator callers in the country.* They learned the art from their father, who had practiced it for years. Predator calling is increasing in popularity today with photographers, resulting in thrilling action photographs as the predators respond to the call.

Motorized hunting of the red fox has become popular in the Western and Midwestern states, where the land is flat and open enough to permit vehicles to be used. Many hunters in those states drive up and down the back roads in their cars during the winter searching for

---

Editor's Note: There is considerable difference of opinion, among sportsmen themselves, about continuing the highly successful and spreading use of the imitated calls of predators, or of their prey, to lure these animals close enough for a shot. The greatly increased kill of predatory species, as a result, has become alarming to all who understand the function of predators in nature.

The predators, as a group or class, are at the thin top of the pyramid of animal numbers, and are usually the least numerous of all. Hawks and owls, now protected by law in most states, and foxes, weasels, and other four-footed predators almost exclusively weed out the sick and crippled among wild game species, which scientists believe helps prevent the spread of their diseases, and keeps game populations in general good health.

Of enormous economic value to cultivated and wild food crops is the role of predators in suppressing the hordes of rats, mice, and other rodents which are often severe competitors of small and big game for grasses, seeds, and other game foods. The rodents and the closely related hares and rabbits are the so-called "key industry" animals on which other animals prey. They are the "buffer" species whose billions bear the brunt of most predation, thus turning predators away from the more difficult-to-catch game species.

Like the professional biologists, game managers, and ecologists, many outdoorsmen know that an inevitable overkill of coyotes, bobcats, and foxes, for example, can cause serious trouble in the wild environment. They fear that unless hunters use restraint in the newly popular, deadly game of predator calling, the practice may be in need of some kind of legislation.

a distant telltale red spot that proclaims a sleeping red fox. When binoculars or a spotting scope authenticates their find, the hunters use high-speed, flat-shooting "varmint" rifles to kill the fox. The .220 Swift, .243, .264, and .270 are the guns most frequently used.

Motorized snowmobiles or sleds are becoming widespread in use, and some hunters use them in pursuit of foxes traveling in deep snow. Other hunters team up with pilots and, using small planes, shoot the foxes from the air. One team in the 1947-48 season shot 425 red foxes and four coyotes.

Needless to say, regular fox hunters are very much against these motorized methods, and I agree with them.

To most fox hunters the dogs are as important as the fox. The first foxhounds were brought over from England, where they had been very effective in hunting the European red fox. Brought into North America, these hounds proved excellent at hunting the gray fox but could not keep up with the native red fox. And so this country developed one of its most important breeds in the dog world, the American foxhound. Some of the most famous of these strains are the Walker, Trigg, July, Trumbo, Goodman, Birdsong, Brooke, Bywater, Buckfield, Redbone, Bluetick, Black-and-Tan, and the Arkansas Traveler.

In the northeastern region of the United States the idea of fox hunting is to kill the fox to obtain its pelt; and where bounties are paid, for the bounty money. When fur prices were high, a single fox pelt brought as much as a week's salary. The fox in that section is looked on as a predator, and many hunters mistakenly believe that each one shot means many more game birds and other animals, as well as less mischief around the chicken yard, though this is now prevented by modern poultry-raising methods.

The fox may be hunted by a single man and dog or a group of men and a pack of dogs. The hound does not have to be a swift runner because frequently a dog that is too fast presses the fox too hard, forcing it to run out of the immediate country. The hound must be tough because the terrain is rough in the mountainous sections where most of these hunts take place. A dog must have a sharp sense of smell because frequently it must start on a cold trail that the fox left hours before. It takes perseverance for the dog to unravel the trail and the tricks used by the fox in an effort to deceive and thwart the hound.

On ground bare of snow the hound is loosed in an area that foxes frequent, but when snow is on the ground, the hunter locates a fresh fox track before putting the hound on the trail. From the direction of travel, the hunter tries to decide where the fox will run or what crossing or barway it will use. He then tries to get there before the fox and the dog arrive. It is important that the dog be an open-trailer and bellow its whereabouts as it trails. Without the dog's voice to guide him, the hunter has no idea where the action is likely to take place. Frequently the fox runs in a different area than the one antici-

A hunter silently awaits the arrival of the fox and hounds.

pated by the hunter, so that the hunter has to move several times in an attempt to get ahead of the fox. At other times the hunter must stand for hours on some bitterly cold, wind-swept slope, watching the horizon through watery eyes and trying to outsmart the fox, which is trying to outsmart both the hunter and the hound. This is the most punishing type of fox hunting; it puts the greatest demand on the hunter, his hound, and the fox, and all rise to meet the occasion.

When the foxhound is working out a cold trail, its occasional baying is enough to let the hunter know that it is on the job and just where it is traveling. As the sound of the baying fills the frosty air, the foxes ahead of the dog start from their beds. The gray fox usually takes to the earth by going down a burrow or seeks out a shelter in the tumbled rocks; the red fox starts to make more tracks. The hound's baying turns to an excited chop when it strikes the fox's hot trail and the chase is on in earnest. The fox, according to its age, experience, and intelligence, uses every trick at its command. It runs in circles, back-tracks, and jumps to one side in an effort to break the scent trail, runs in water, walks along old wooden fences or railroad rails, and seeks out all the odorous spots it knows. The fox instinctively knows that the hound cannot track it across freshly manured, plowed, burned, or limed fields in which the fox's odor is lost. It knows that water washes away scent and that mingling with cattle, sheep, pigs, or horses will cover its scent. The fox runs along highways or seek out spots where oil, gasoline, or other chemical odors will mask its own. A wise hound also knows many of these tricks, and when it loses the fox's scent, it makes ever-expanding circles till the scent is picked up again. Many times the delay means a fox lost to the hunter and his dog; at other times it merely gives the fox a rest.

In cold, snowy weather, the fox soon abandons the sunny side of the mountain and crosses to the north side or runs the ridges. On the ridge tops the wind usually blows strongly enough to keep the snow shallow so the fox will not tire so readily. It is also colder on the ridge,

Red fox hunters walk through the woods, with hound in tow.

and when the temperature drops to zero, it is almost impossible for a dog to follow the scent. Although the north side of the mountain may have more snow, it is frequently crusted enough to support the weight of the fox but not of the hounds. The fox knows of every stream, river, or pond and runs on them because no scent will be left by it on the smooth ice. Sometimes the fox deliberately runs on thin ice which breaks under the greater weight of the hound, which may drown in the icy waters. Woven wire fences are a great help to the fox because it can easily slip through the squares while the hound has to go over the fence or around it, or through a gate or other opening. The foxes seem to know this.

If not pressed too closely, the fox stays within an area of a couple of square miles. It does not want to leave its home place because it is at a disadvantage when it is forced into new territory. The hunter, too, hopes that the fox does not run away into new country because then he is denied any chance of getting a shot.

While the hound is unraveling the fox's trail, the hunter remains as motionless as possible on his stand because many times the fox is some distance ahead of the hound. Even though the fox can hear the hound in the distance, it is at all times alert to the possibility of danger from the unseen hunter. The hunter that stamps his feet or flails his arms in an effort to restore the flow of blood to his frost-nipped hands and feet seldom gets a shot, as the fox is alert to the slightest movement. Sometimes the fox's presence is given away to the hunter by crows that delight in pestering the fox by flying overhead and diving down at it, cawing madly all the while.

Many foxes make the mistake of using the same tricks and routes on the same dog on successive hunts. The smart hunter, knowing that the fox may do this, has a better chance the second time he hunts it because he knows what the fox is likely to do and where and how he can intercept it.

When the fox tires of playing or cannot outwit the hound, it falls back on its speed to carry it beyond the dog's reach. Some foxes have been known to disgorge the contents of their stomach, if forced to run too hard. Thus lightened, they can travel faster and longer. When ice balls up on the fox's feet, it must stop long enough to chew it away before it continues its flight. However, the hound's bare pads are more likely to get cut or bruised, and this may slow it down.

A fox chased into a new area is a worried fox because it does not know the terrain. After the hunt is over, it tries to return to its own range as soon as possible.

In the middle of winter after the foxes have paired, they sometimes run the hounds in relays. When one fox tires, it seeks out its mate, which then runs in front of the hounds and leads them away on a chase while the first fox gets a rest. Just before parturition the female, heavy with young, goes into the earth in a den when hard pressed. Under such circumstances the male often leads the hounds away. In late spring and summer either of the parents will do the same thing to lead the hounds from the pups.

Now that the price of fur has declined, so has much of the fox hunting in the Northeast. Many of the men that I knew who had good hounds and hunted regularly no longer do so.

In the southern and midwestern section of the red fox's range, the hunters engage in "jug hunts." The object of these hunts is conviviality, and the fox is never killed except by accident. These hunters select their dogs as much for their voices as for their speed and noses.

Some of the hounds have bass voices, others are tenors, while still others are baritones. Some are known as squealers, choppers, bellers, and buglers. These fox hunters wax enthusiastic as they expansively describe the silver-toned notes of their dogs. They may be at a loss for the proper words to describe a beautiful woman, but they can eloquently describe the voices of their hounds in words that other hunters understand and appreciate. The music of a pack of hounds in full cry is a spine-tingling, heart-warming experience that lives in the hearts and minds of these men long after the hunt is over.

The hunting is usually done at night when a group of hunters get together with as many of their neighbors and friends as care to join them. The hounds are loosed while the men build a bonfire to ward off the night's chill. Such a hunt is called a "jug hunt" because a container of liquor of that shape is often passed around as an addi-

133

tional chill preventer. The hounds hunt far and wide, and the progress of the hunt is unfolded to the hunters by the sounds of their dogs. Each man knows the voices of his hounds and can tell by their cries whether the trail is cold or hot, and much good-natured rivalry springs up according to whose hound is leading the pack.

This is a most democratic hunt, and anyone and his dogs are made to feel welcome. If the hunt is a long one, some of the men and their hounds may join the group or drop out according to their time schedules. It is easy to release the hounds but difficult to call them back. The hunters usually call the hounds in by blowing on a steer or goat horn, but the excited dogs may not respond. Many a hunter may leave his coat in the woods at the place where the hunt started. When he comes back on the morrow, he usually finds the hound curled up on it, expectantly awaiting him.

Formalized fox hunting goes back in history in England to about the year 1300. Riding to the hounds was always considered a sport of royalty and the upper classes. This kind of hunting became ritualistic —the rules governing the hunt and its etiquette are still followed today.

In England, Lord Baltimore encouraged his settlers sailing for America to take their dogs there. A good friend of Lord Baltimore's, Robert Brooke, did just that. On June 30, 1650, Mr. Brooke settled in what is now Queen Annes County, Maryland on an estate joining that of his mentor. In addition to his wife, two daughters, and eight sons, Mr. Brooke brought twenty-eight grooms, including kennel men, whippers-in and a huntsman, to take care of his blooded horses and his large pack of English foxhounds. The Brooke hounds of today are directly descended from this original pack.

George Washington loved the fox hunt and made 106 entries about the sport in his book *Where and How My Time is Spent*. Washington, while overseeing his plantation, usually rode his favorite hunter, Magnolia, and was accompanied by his colored man, Billy Lee, on Chinkling. The two hounds, Vulcan and Stately, were allowed to run loose, and a fox hunt was enjoyed whenever one could be started.

According to Joseph Neff Ewing, chairman of the Masters of Fox-hounds Association of America headquartered in Philadelphia, there are over one hundred registered fox-hunting organizations in the United States, and no one knows how many are unregistered. Most of the dogs used in the packs of such organizations still retain strong bloodlines of the English foxhounds because they are more tractable and are more easily trained to the commands of the huntsman. The horses used for fox hunting are known as hunters and are trained and selected for their ability to jump fences and other obstacles. A good horse enjoys the hunt and seems as excited as the hunter about it. Some riders hunt foxes in order to ride, while the dyed-in-the-wool hunter rides to hunt foxes. The entire proceedings are under the management of the hunt master, who is usually dressed in "pinks," the customary scarlet hunting outfit, while the rest of the participants may be similarly attired if they so choose.

The fox may be killed if the dogs can catch it, although it is never killed by the hunters. The first hunter to reach the fox, if the dogs do catch it, is entitled to keep its "brush" as a trophy. The novice hunters, in on their first kill, are "blooded" by having a drop of blood from the fox's tail dotted on the center of their foreheads. If foxes are scarce and the hunters get to the fox in time to save it, they do so for the sport it will provide on another hunt. Many fox hunting clubs import foxes from other regions and release them to ensure having foxes to hunt. This practice does not endear the fox hunters to the small game hunters or poultry farmers whose lands may be adjacent to the hunt-club property.

My good friend Art Wilkens told me about a thrilling red fox hunt that he saw on land owned by a club at Golden Bridge, New York. Art and a companion, Frank Coster, had permission to hunt the estate for rabbits and were walking beside one of the many stone fences that separated all the fields. About the middle of the morning they could hear the bellowing of a pack of hounds that had a fox on the run. The tumult kept coming closer, and they soon perceived a large red fox coming toward them, followed at quite a distance by the pack and the mounted hunters. Being on a slight hill, Art and Frank had ringside seats for the show that took place just below them.

The fox ran across a lower field and through the gate or barway in the stone wall. Turning sharply, it ran alongside the wall for about 150 feet, then suddenly jumped to the top of it. Crouching on its belly, the fox crawled back along the top of the wall to the gate through which it had previously run, and then lay down. In the meantime, the hounds ran through the gate, hot on the fox's trail. When the lead dogs came to the spot where the fox had leaped to the wall, they milled about trying to pick up its scent.

As soon as the last dog had passed through the gate, the fox leaped to the ground and ran back through the middle of the approaching hunters. Confusion reigned as the hunters pulled up their horses and tried to call in the dogs. By the time they could get the dogs to the spot, much of the fox's scent had been destroyed by the churning hooves of the horses. The fox, meanwhile, slipped through a fence and escaped by crossing a highway. Then it disappeared into the heavily wooded mountainside beyond.

Another red fox got away by putting its life literally in the hands of the Lord. Tiring after a long chase, it dashed into the open door of a church and, like most late-comers, ducked into one of the pews in the rear. When the hounds came clamoring up the steps of the church, they were quickly evicted, and the door was slammed shut. Both the hunters and the congregation agreed that the fox had a right to the sanctuary it had sought.

Other creatures hunt the red fox, too, at this time of year. Both the coyote and the wolf are enemies of the fox and, being larger and stronger, tire less easily in soft, deep snow. Luckily for the fox, the

The lynx preys on the red fox in winter when its large foot pads allow it to walk on top of soft snow while the red fox sinks in.

wolf's range is shrinking, although the coyote's is expanding. In some parts of New York's Adirondack Mountains, the influx of coyotes is providing the red fox with real competition for survival.

From time immemorial the canine and feline families have been deadly enemies. Under most circumstances the fox is too quick to be caught by either the bobcat or the lynx. In the winter all of this changes. In deep, soft snow the red fox finds the going hard, as its small feet offer it little support. The lynx in particular has exceptionally large feet that act as snowshoes to support its weight and make it look as though it is walking on four dust mops. Not only can the lynx walk on top of the snow, but it outweighs the fox three or four to one. The lynx seldom eats any of the foxes, but it does go out of its way to kill them.

Like all animals, the fox is prone to accidents. In December, 1962, a red fox in Spotsylvania County, Virginia, thrust its head into a fallen tree cavity, found that it could not extricate itself, and died.

By midwinter the red fox population, like the population of most other wild creatures, reaches its lowest point. But already Nature has begun to ensure the continuation of the species. The testicles of the male fox begin to enlarge, and by late November the formation of

137

sperms, has taken place. From this period until late April, living sperm will be present in his semen and the male is capable of breeding. The only outward manifestation of the male's spermatogenesis is that he now actively seeks a mate for the coming year, although the female does not usually come into her heat until January or February. Both the male and female red fox are sexually mature at ten months of age, although the yearling females usually breed a little later in the year than do the mature females. Sometimes a yearling female will not breed at all during her first year.

The sharp terrier-like bark of the red fox may be heard at almost any season, but it is heard much more frequently during the winter. The yapping bark of the red fox in winter, like the hooting of the great horned owl, is about the wildest sound that Easterners are likely to hear. The Westerners have their coyote, which howls at all times of the year, but it is only in the Far North that the howl of the wolf is still heard. Usually the fox gives two or three yaps, tapering off with a slurring "yaaaaa" at the end. Occasionally the red fox, the female in particular, gives a bloodcurdling shriek.

At all times of the year the fox, like the other members of the canine family, makes scent stations by urinating and sometimes defecating on conspicuous tufts of grass, old bones, sticks, and stones. These places are very easy to see in winter because of the yellow crystals of urine, and are used as a means of communication between the foxes. The female also uses these scent posts but not with the frequency that the male does. Researchers following fox tracks in the snow have found evidence that a male had urinated forty to fifty times in a single night. I once observed that a male red fox had urinated on six scent posts in one trip across a 1,000-foot field, his tracks meandering to each clump of grass. In new snow the sex of the fox may be told by the tracks at the scent posts. The female usually squats to urinate so that her stains show between her hind feet tracks. The male usually, but not always, raises a rear leg and is more able to eject urine on whatever object

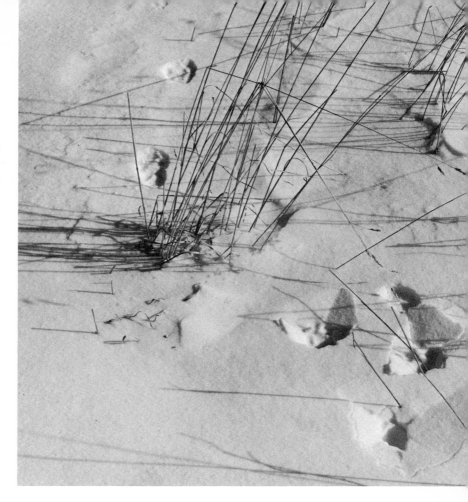

The red fox makes scent posts on tufts of grass or other conspicuous places as a means of communication. Note the urine crystals.

is being used as a scent station.

Adult foxes usually pair with their mates of the previous season, but mortality is so high that they frequently seek new ones. As with most species, some females are more desirable than others, and fights between the males competing for them are common.

When two males aggressively approach each other, their tails are an indication of their emotions, and the male with the larger tail has the advantage because he appears larger to his rival. The foxes may circle each other with their tails carried in a horseshoe shape. The tails are used for sparring, and one or the other of the foxes flicks his tail in his opponent's face and tries to bite him while he is temporarily unable to see. Sometimes one male hits the other with his rump in an attempt to knock him off his feet. Often the males rear upright on their hind legs, putting their front feet on each other's chests. They

139

Two red foxes fight with each other.

then attempt to push each other backward at the same time, making lightning-fast slashes at each other with their teeth. All this is accompanied by much growling, hissing, and squalling. The fights are seldom fatal, as the fox losing out retreats at high speed, pursued by the victorious male for a short distance. One pair of red foxes fighting in New York State lost their footing and fell over a cliff; the fall to the rocks below killed them both.

The red fox's daily winter range has been calculated at 1.4 square miles. An unmated fox covers a much greater area. As there are usually more females than males, the unmated female at this time travels great distances and can often be heard squalling her frustrations to

140

the world. One red vixen in heat was seen playing with a male dog on the ice at Lake Wallenpaupack in Pennsylvania. Although breeding could take place, fertilization could not.

After red foxes have paired, the male and female are almost inseparable, and often play together. Their dual tracks in the snow reveal their constancy and their every movement. Cooperation by them in hunting is common and may be an important survival factor behind the fox's long courtship. Joe Taylor caught a red female in a trap during the breeding season and was surprised to find the male lying on a hummock nearby.

The female red fox is monoestrus, having just one heat period per year. She is in estrus for fourteen days but will only accept the male during the middle of that period. At that time, her vulva is greatly swollen and whitish in color. During the female's receptive period, which is of a four-day duration, repeated matings will take place, each lasting about fifteen minutes. The male fox has a knot on the middle of his penis that swells after its insertion into the female's vagina,

From mid-December the red foxes pair up, and double sets of tracks are seen.

This den has been cleaned out by a red fox. Note the dirt and other debris visible around the entrance.

locking the pair together. This coupling allows for a more positive placement of the male's sperm. Most foxes breed in the early morning. The majority of the females are in estrus during the last of January through the middle of February. However, T. Hannon, of Livingston, Wisconsin, saw a pair of red foxes copulating on December 16, 1948.

After breeding, the pair investigate all suitable dens in their area. Three or four of these dens are cleaned out and enlarged, although only one is used. The rest are held in reserve. As the ground is usually snow-covered while the renovating of the dens takes place, the sites are very conspicuous because the dirt excavated from them can be seen from a long distance. The easiest way to locate future whelping dens is to track the foxes on snow during the breeding season, noting which dens are being prepared for occupation. Later when it is time for the pups to come out of the den, all these prospective sites can be revisited and the young easily located.

Both the male and the female fox work on enlarging the dens, but the female does the bulk of it. Crawling in and out of the den causes the fox's fur to wear and appear rubbed because the ends of the hairs have broken off. The fur of the male usually appears more worn than that of the female, even though she spends far more time in the den than he does. With warm weather, the foxes will start to shed their winter coats.

As parturition nears, the female travels less and remains in or near the favored den, responding to the stirring embryos felt within her body.

The rubbed rump of this red fox is a result of crawling in and out of the den.

The Red Fox and Man

ABOUT 40,000,000 years ago a weasel-like mammal evolved which is known to paleontologists as Miacis. Miacis is the common ancestor of all the carnivores, including both the dog and the bear, although when it first appeared it apparently resembled neither. In addition to its lithe, weasel-like body, it had short legs and an exceptionally long tail, a tail as long or longer than its entire body and head length combined.

With the passage of time those first carnivores evolved into a creature scientists call Cynodictis, which retained the general body shape of Miacis but had longer legs. Evidently the first carnivores lived in trees but gradually left their arboreal homes to range on the open grass lands. As an adaptation to catching faster prey on the ground, the carnivores evolved longer legs, compact paws, and powerful back muscles.

During this period of evolution, the bear's ancestors are thought to have separated from the canine's ancestors. Ancestral bears became large, heavy mammals that lost their speed but gained great strength. The canine line evolved into Cynodesmus, from which all the modern wolves, foxes, and dogs have descended. Because of the canine's cursorial way of life, the legs became even longer, the lungs larger, and a social behavior or gregariousness became the rule rather than the exception. The red fox is one of the exceptions.

The canine's next-in-line ancestor was Tomarctus, a mammal that had the appearance, habits, and characteristics of today's canines besides much more intelligence than any of the earlier forms. It was at this stage of evolution that the foxes split apart from the wolves, coyotes, and dogs. Since then they have come down through time as a separate genus.

This all leads up to another controversy: the status of the red fox in North America. From the records of the early explorers and settlers we know that foxes were found in most of the English colonies, but were they red foxes or gray foxes?

In 1602 the English explorer Bartholomew visited the southern New England coast. A member of his party by the name of Brereton related, "So we spent the rest of the day in trading with the Indians for furres, which are beavers, lynxes, marterns, otters, wild-cat skins, very large and deep furre, black foxes, etc., etc."

In 1603, Martin Pring explored the same region and reported, "The beasts here are bears, wolves, foxes, etc."

Captain John Smith, on one of his famous exploratory trips from Jamestown, Virginia, visited the New England coast in 1615-16 and wrote, "Of bevers, otters, martins, blacke foxes and furres of price, may yearly be had six or seven thousand." He later mentioned "foxes both blacke and other."

William Wood, in 1634, mentioned foxes in a poem that he wrote about the mammals of New England, but he did not mention color.

Bradford's *History of the New England Plantations, Book II,* published in 1636, mentioned "Black Fox skins" on page 344.

However, Thomas Morton, in 1637, wrote of New England, "The Foxes are of two coloures; the one redd, the other gray; these feede on fish, and are of good furre; they doe not stinke, as the Foxes of England."

Here, then, is the first record which mentions that there were red foxes in New England in the earliest days of white exploration. It is also the first record specifically mentioning the gray fox. All the previous records refer to either just foxes or black foxes. I am inclined to believe that the other records, in mentioning black foxes, are really referring to the gray foxes. I base my argument on another early record.

In 1643 Roger Williams, who had founded Rhode Island in 1636, was returning to England to secure a Royal Charter for the towns of Providence, Newport, and Portsmouth. While at sea he wrote a book called *A Key to the Language of the Indians of New England*. Williams was fluent in the language of the Narragansett Indians and recorded that their name for the red fox was "mishquashim," while their name for the gray fox was "pequawas." He also mentioned that the Indians had seen black foxes but had never succeeded in taking any of them.

Many uninformed persons, on seeing a gray fox, call it a silver fox or a black fox because of its dark pelage, a confusion which has always existed. Silver or black foxes have been taken in the Adirondack Mountains, but New England is on the very southern fringe of these melanistic red foxes. The Hudson Bay Company's records show that only 1 per cent of all the foxes taken by their trading posts are silver or black foxes, making it even more likely that the black foxes of New England which the early explorers described were actually gray foxes. The clincher is found in Roger Williams's statement that the Narragansett Indians had seen the real silver or black foxes and, though these Indians had inhabited New England for generations, they had never succeeded in taking any of them and didn't even have a name for them. This would indicate that the real black or silver foxes were very scarce. That the Indians were successful in taking the gray foxes is shown by the fact that they had traded "black" pelts to the early explorers.

It is known that red fox remains have been found in pre-Columbian archaeological sites in New York, Massachusetts, and Rhode Island. These remains are at least 1,500 years old, and may be as much as 6,000 years old. No one has ever questioned the fact that there were native red foxes in Canada and northern New England, but at the time of the coming of the white man they were not reported south of New England or east of Illinois. The unbroken hardwood forests of the mid-Atlantic states evidently provided an impenetrable barrier to the red fox's range expansion. Archaeological excavations in these mid-Atlantic states have failed to disclose the remains of any red fox, although gray fox remains are common.

Peter Kalm, the Swedish botanist who traveled extensively in the New World during the middle of the eighteenth century, wrote on November 7, 1748, that there were two species of foxes in the English Colonies, one gray and the other red. The gray foxes were native, common to the southern regions, although a few were found as far north as Ontario, where the French called them Virginian foxes. He also stated that John Bartram and others of Philadelphia, assured him that the Leni-Lenape Indians of New Jersey and Pennsylvania were unanimous in their testimony that they had never seen a red fox before they were brought in by the Europeans.

The red fox is a native of North America.

The first record of the importation into North America of the European red fox goes back to about 1650 when a captain of a Maryland tobacco schooner was instructed to bring back eight pairs of red foxes on his next trip from Liverpool, England. When the foxes were delivered, they were liberated along Maryland's Eastern Shore. In the early 1700's one of the English governors of New York also imported red foxes from England and turned them loose on Long Island so that he could hunt them with horses and hounds. The foxes multiplied and spread to the mainland when the ice provided a bridge from the island. Other importations were made, and red foxes were released in New Jersey and Virginia.

Two things occurred simultaneously with the settlement of the land by the Europeans: the larger predators such as the cougar and the wolf were killed off, and the virgin forests were opened. Freed from natural predation and encouraged by the increase in cottontail rabbits, mice, and other food that accompanied the opening up of the land, the red fox quickly extended its range southward and westward. Meeting and breeding with the native red fox, apparently, the imported red fox population was gradually assimilated and lost its identity. The red fox is a forest edge or open land animal; it still avoids virgin forests or treeless prairies but is steadily expanding its range over other habitats. In the western mountains the red fox lives right up to the snow line at 11,000-12,000 feet elevation.

Since 1820 the North American red fox has been known as *Vulpes fulva,* a name given by A. G. Desmarest. It was considered a separate species until 1959, when the studies undertaken by Charles S. Churcher of the Royal Ontario Museum in Toronto, Canada, suggested that all the Holarctic red foxes are one. Although cranial and dental variations do occur between the species, they are clinal variations. The red foxes of Eastern Europe are as different from Siberian red foxes as Alaskan red foxes are from Labrador red foxes. However, despite minor differences, all the species have such a great degree of similarity that they

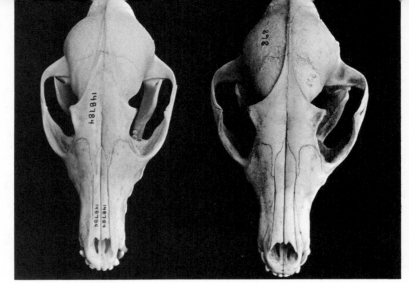

The skull of the North American red fox is shown at left; the skull of the European red fox at right.

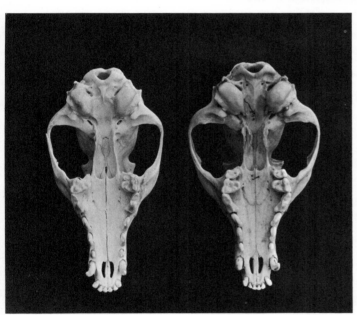

The underside skull of the North American red fox is at left; the underside skull of the European red fox at right.

The skull of the European red fox appears above; the skull of the North American red fox below.

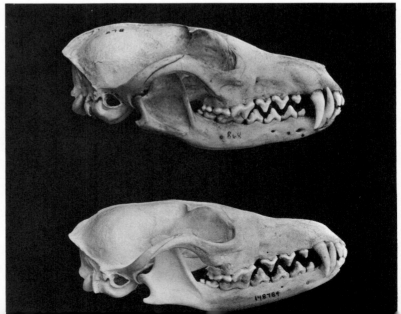

are now recognized as one and have reverted to the original name of *Vulpes vulpes*.

There are twelve subspecies of the red fox in North America. The taxonomic distinction of the red fox subspecies, or geographic forms, becomes increasingly complex with the passage of time because of man's interference with natural conditions. By changing the environment, man has sponsored the range extension of the red fox. Red fox remains have been dated in Idaho as being 14,000 years old, but the red fox was exceedingly scarce there in recent times until 1891. With the eradication of its natural enemies, the red fox in Idaho began to increase, an increase that has skyrocketed since 1960. In addition, man has transported subspecies beyond their natural limitations and boundaries by importing and releasing red foxes for sport. Because of these changes in the distribution of the red fox, only the experts can really tell the subspecies apart. Generally, the largest red foxes are in Minnesota; the smallest are in Washington State. The red fox on Kodiak Island, Alaska, has the bushiest tail, those in Utah have the longest tail, those in Washington State have the shortest. But again these are variations among the subspecies. Please consult the range map to ascertain the territory designated for each of the twelve subspecies.

There is an old saying among hunters and trappers that when the gray fox moves into an area, the red fox moves out—the implication being that the gray fox is able to beat a red fox in an actual fight. I know of no one who has seen the two foxes fight under natural conditions. I once put a gray fox in a large cage with a red fox until I could get another cage built. The red fox should have been dominant because he had been living in the cage and it was his home territory. However, after a flurry of yapping, biting, and shoving, the gray was boss of the cage. The gray fox did not push its advantage and continue to clobber the red; it was just the dominant fox.

Leon Kitchen told me that he was checking his traps one day and saw, as he approached, that he had caught a red fox. The fox did not notice Leon because it had its attention focused on a gray fox that was circling around it. The gray fox's hair was standing on end so that it was bristled up to almost twice its normal size. The gray fox circled the red fox six times while Leon watched. The red fox sat unmoving, just watching the gray, waiting for it to make the first move. Leon had no way of knowing how long this circling had been going on, nor did he see the outcome, because he shot at the gray fox and missed and the gray ran off.

This episode does not prove which fox would win in a fight, but it does prove that the gray fox is the more aggressive of the two, or it would not have approached the red. Although the red fox has the advantage of having longer canine teeth than the gray fox, its skin is much thinner and is more easily torn. Because of this thin skin, hunters find that the red fox is easier to kill than a gray fox, and this would be a disadvantage in a fight between the two.

From personal experience I know that the red fox avoids areas that the gray fox utilizes. When a fox is trapped, it urinates frequently in its struggle to get loose. I have often caught gray foxes after having first caught a red fox at the same spot, but it was very seldom that I caught a red fox after catching the gray fox first. All the canines mark their areas or territories by urinating on conspicuous landmarks, creating scent posts. It is my belief that the red was hesitant to violate what it considered the gray's area as proclaimed by its urine at the trap site.

Over the years I have seen the grays move into what was formerly red fox territory and literally take it over, but I do not believe that the take-over had anything to do with the animosity between the two foxes. What had occurred, although too slowly for most people to notice, was that the habitat had changed.

In the northeastern United States, we have already noted how the red fox increased its range as the virgin forests were cut down. The gray fox had lived in those forests for centuries, as is shown by its remains in most of the archaeological excavations. As the forest were eliminated, the red foxes moved on to the farmland and the grays moved out. They were not chased out by the reds but by the settler's ax. Within the past forty to fifty years, the gray fox has been spreading rapidly northward again, reclaiming some of its ancestral territory, as the marginal farms that have been abandoned in the Adirondack and New England regions grow back into mature forests. And so we see that the key to the red fox's range is man's activities.

The key to the red fox's population in the United States is not governed by man but by a natural cycle and to a large extent by the style preferences of women. When long-haired furs are fashionable, women create a demand for fox skins and the red fox population is curtailed or reduced because of increased trapping pressure. This does not hold true in the Canadian wilderness. There the native trappers have to trap whatever they can catch whether the price of fur is high or low. The fluctuation in the number of fox skins taken in Canada is governed by the natural cycle of the foxes and not by the dictates of fashion.

The red foxes in North America are subject to two natural cycles of different timing; the reason for one is understood, the other is not. In the United States and in the lower tier of the Canadian provinces, the red fox reaches peak populations every ten years, with the peak being reached on or about the years ending with the number 5. Ernest Thompson Seton is credited with having first brought attention to this cycle, which is based on the actual fur returns of the Hudson Bay Company's records. Many wildlife cycles are linked to food supplies and overpopulation with the resultant stresses of overcrowding, diseases, and predation, but apparently the red fox cycle, at least in the United States, is not. The all-time high for the red fox population in the United States occurred in 1944-45 from Iowa and Minnesota east to New York State and in 1946-47 for New York, Pennsylvania, New Jersey, and the New England states.

In 1947, as the red fox population was declining in Wisconsin, biologists there found that the foxes showed signs of emaciation and poor fur quality and the bone marrow showed signs of starvation. This was strictly a local phenomenon because investigators have found no other area with similar evidence that could be construed as being the cause of the decline. I know from personal experience that when the red foxes declined in my own area, those that were caught were in as good a condition as when they had been at their peak; no disease was apparent, and food was plentiful. Yet the red fox population did decline, and I don't know why. Nor has anyone else given us a satisfactory answer.

The red foxes of the arctic regions of Scandinavia, Siberia, and North America reach peak populations in a four-year cycle that coincides with the four-year cycle of the voles and lemmings. These small rodents suffer tremendous population fluctuations every four years. They are the main food of the arctic red foxes, and when the voles and lemmings are plentiful, so are the foxes. When the rodent population falls, it pulls down the fox population with it. During the so-called crash periods in their food supply of rodents red foxes in the arctic have been known to travel hundreds of miles southward in an attempt to find food. As the rodent crash is widespread, few of the foxes survive, and even fewer live to make the trek back north. The surviving resident voles, lemmings, and foxes recover and rise to a peak again four years later.

These wildlife cycles and population fluctuations are only now being understood by the biologists and are a source of great confusion to many laymen. Some fluctuations confuse everyone. The ring-necked pheasant population fluctuations in the United States are just such a source of confusion; they fit no known pattern or cycle. From the 1920's, the pheasant population rose steadily, reaching a peak between 1936 and 1941 which varied in different parts of its range. From those peak years the pheasants skidded to an extreme low in the mid-1940's. The decline was so rapid, widespread, and decisive that everyone concerned with wildlife throughout the pheasant's range searched frantically for a cause. It was during this same crash period of the pheasants

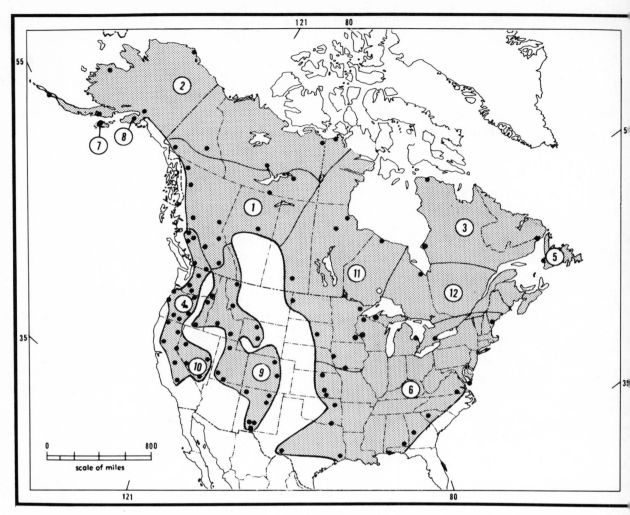

Distribution of red fox subspecies (Vulpes fulva) *throughout North America**

1. *V. f. abeitorum*	4. *V. f. cascadensis*	7. *V. f. harrimani*	10. *V. f. necator*
2. *V. f. alascensis*	5. *V. f. deletrix*	8. *V. f. kenaiensis*	11. *V. f. regalis*
3. *V. f. bangsi*	6. *V. f. fulva*	9. *V. f. macroura*	12. *V. f. rubricosa*

that the red fox was reaching its peak numbers, and this coincidence was seized upon as significant—that the predations of the red fox were the cause of the pheasant decline. The red fox was branded the culprit.

Because no one could positively state that the red fox was not respon-

*From E. Raymond Hall and Keith R. Kelson, *The Mammals of North America*. Copyright © 1959 The Ronald Press Company, New York.

Occasionally red foxes catch ring-necked pheasants.

sible for the decline in the pheasants, the greatest concentrated effort and study ever made of the fox was begun. Most of the biological data and scientific literature that we have on the red fox today was produced during those years of study. When all the evidence was in, the fox was completely exonerated.

One of the many important facts that came to light was that the greatest concentrations of pheasants never coincided with the greatest concentration of foxes. Pheasants are strictly inhabitants of farmland; the richer and heavier the soil, the better. The fox, on the other hand,

155

prefers the marginal lands and the light soil that is suitable for den sites.

The most dramatic vindication of the red fox as a threat to pheasants came from Pelee Island, in the western end of Lake Erie. The bulk of the island's 10,000 acres is under cultivation, and it has long supported an abnormally high pheasant population. When the pheasant population on the mainland crashed to a low, so did the population on the island. However, the crash on Pelee Island could not possibly have been blamed on the red fox because there are no foxes on the island.

I am chief gamekeeper for the Coventry Hunting Club, one of the largest clubs of its kind in the State of New Jersey. The club is a community project, and we have about 5,000 acres of land ideally located between the Delaware River and the Kittatinny Mountains. Pheasants do not breed naturally in our valley, and so we purchase about 1,800 of them and release them periodically throughout the season. The valley is not ideal pheasant habitat; we now realize that it is impossible to raise pheasants naturally, and so we stock them for shooting. Because we are releasing pheasants into an area that is unfamiliar to them, they are highly susceptible to predation by foxes, hawks, and owls. Many of our hunters, seeing fox-eaten pheasant carcasses, are erroneously convinced that pheasants everywhere are as subject to severe predation by foxes. What these hunters fail to realize is that we are introducing the pheasants into a hostile environment under artificial conditions.

During the period of the intense study of red foxes by biologists, they studied in particular the food habits of the red fox. Material was gathered from the actual stomach contents of dead foxes or by collecting fox scats. Of the two methods, the collecting of scats was the more accurate because the fox had been a free agent, undisturbed in its natural habitat at the time it had voided.

The study of fox stomach contents was not so productive and was sometimes misleading. Most of the stomachs studied were obtained from foxes that had been trapped. Quite frequently they were empty because the fox was often caught at the start of its hunting activities. Often the reason the fox was caught was that its stomach was empty

This fox-cached pheasant was found and eaten by crows.

and the fox had been attracted to the bait. At other times the stomachs contained grass and foreign material that the fox had swallowed while it was trying to free itself.

It is well known that a fox eats carrion, yet it cannot be proved from its stomach contents that it killed the animal it fed on, or scavenged the remains. Biologists tend to discount material from fox stomachs or scats as being prey if they find that carrion beetles have been ingested with it, yet prey that the foxes kill and cache often contains carrion beetles when eaten at a later time. Gradually, however, enough data was gathered to give a reasonably accurate compilation of red fox foods.

One thing must be remembered when studying the fox's stomach contents or its scats: the red fox is an opportunist. The evidence from any one sample only shows what that particular fox ate at that particular time in that particular area, because that was what was available. It is too easy to jump to conclusions—painstaking research is required to get the facts.

In 1936 biologists in New Hampshire estimated that the farmers in that state lost 72,238 chickens to predators. Proof of this predation was the number of chicken carcasses found at fox dens and chicken remains found in stomach contents and scat collections. As the price of fur was dropping, predation on chickens increased because of a decrease in trapping.

Two interesting thoughts come to mind. First, I am sure that if studies of the red fox's food habits were undertaken today, the incidence of poultry would be much less than previously. Poultry farming has become such big business and so efficient that the fox doesn't have access to the poultry that it had a scant ten to fifteen years ago.

Second, although the cottontail rabbit is the most important food item in the red fox's diet for a large part of the year, perhaps the fox doesn't really care for rabbit. Statistics have proved that the rabbit figures prominently in the fox's diet only when other foods are not available.

From the very earliest day of settlement in the United States, the various forms of governments—colonial, state, and local—have tried to control the numbers and depredations of wild mammals and birds by placing a bounty on them. This archaic and fruitless form of control is still practiced in many parts of the country today and has resulted in the squandering of untold millions of dollars. The avowed purpose of bounties has always been to control predation, but, with few exceptions, the attempt has failed completely.

The fox tracks entering on the right provide mute testimony that a fox has discovered the rabbit tracks on the left.

Proponents of bounties are quick to point out that the wolf and the cougar were wiped out over much of their range at an early date because of bounties. Yet these proponents cannot prove that the wolf and the cougar were not wiped out because of the encroachment and destruction of their habitat by the advance of civilization instead of by bounties. The bobcat, the fox, and the coyote are the most commonly bountied animals, but their numbers have never been controlled by this system, although many states have paid out millions of dollars trying. Today the bobcat is still bountied in thirteen states, foxes in twelve states, and the coyote in eleven. Ninety per cent of all bounty money is paid for foxes.

As I have said before, managing game is the easiest part of game management; the most difficult task is to manage people. To manage people, they must be educated, and it is hard to tear apart the many myths and misinformation about our wildlife that they have believed and passed down through the ages. Nothing raises such a furor as trying to educate the general public to the advisability of harvesting surplus doe deer or the inadvisability of paying a bounty on foxes.

I realize that there are many side advantages to the payment of bounties because for years I trapped foxes, mainly for the bounty. The price of fur had dropped so low that without the bounty subsidies, I could not have afforded to take the time to trap. Bounties do augment the income of many people living in rural sections, they do help to defray the cost of maintaining the hounds of the fox hunter, and they do encourage sportsmen to hunt the fox, but these reasons are *not* justification for the bounty system. Statistics have proved that most of the foxes bountied would have been killed by the sportsmen anyway in conjunction with whatever sport in which the hunter was engaged. Almost every rabbit-, grouse-, or deer-hunter is going to try to kill every fox he sees, and the payment of a bounty neither prompts nor deters this action. Some of the foxes that are bountied have been killed accidentally by automobiles. This is another reason that foxes seldom, if ever, show up in tables of wildlife killed on the highways. Because of the bounty, they are quickly gathered up and presented for payment. In some of the states that pay bounties, it is illegal to present foxes killed by automobiles for payment, but who can prove how the fox was killed?

The tendency to fraud is another indictment against bounties. Some individual foxes have been presented for bounties two or three times. Often dead foxes are brought from states which do not pay a bounty to states that do. Occasionally, dog and raccoon scalps are presented to an unknowing clerk for bounty payment on foxes. In warm weather when carcasses tend to "ripen" overnight, the clerk is often inclined to take the trapper's word that all animals in the sack are those of foxes rather than examining them closely himself. At one time one state paid a bounty on fox tails, so many trappers cut off the fox's tail and then released the fox to continue to live as a breeder.

The bounty system has never succeeded because no trapper ever tries to wipe out his source of income. That would be like killing the goose that laid the golden eggs. The trapper always leaves some seed stock. When I was trapping, I never tried to trap all the foxes in an area but would take only the surplus foxes that were living on the farmlands. It just didn't pay to backpack up in the mountainous areas to try to catch every fox. As the fox takes the surplus game, man takes the surplus of foxes. Because of this, each inaccessible area served as a reservoir of foxes. As the foxes on the farm were trapped, those on the adjacent areas expanded their ranges and moved in. Nature abhors a vacuum and does its best to fill each niche.

Actually, it is the fox population and the country's economic situation that control the number of foxes bountied. When the fox population is high, more foxes are bountied; when the population is down, so are the fox returns because, usually, the bounty is not large enough to make the effort to catch them worthwhile. In these days of high wages and virtually no unemployment, the bounty is not an inducement to trap animals on which bounties are paid.

Many state game departments vacillate between paying bounties and stopping such payments. Some game departments would like to follow the lead of the more enlightened states and dispose of the bounty system but are not allowed to do so because the bounty is a political football. The foxes can't vote, but the bounty recipients do. In rural sections, politicians have to support the bounty whether they approve of it or not because that is what their constituents want.

No game department in any state should be under political jurisdiction. Administrative funds should come from hunting and trapping license sales or be given to the department by the state legislature with no limitations on their use. Only then will game managers be able to manage game for the greatest good of the greatest number of people and put a stop to the shameful waste of money paid out in bounties.

Today many game departments have fully realized the fox's role as a predator and are no longer interested in eliminating all foxes. Some states have trapper-instructors while others have predator-control men. On receipt of a complaint of actual fox damage, the former group teaches the landowner how to cope with the situation while the predator-control men trap the individual animal or animals doing the actual damage. This, I feel, is the wisest way to handle the situation— individual elimination of troublesome animals, not the attempted eradication of all.

A new method of biological control of foxes is under experimentation in several sections of the country. Prior to the breeding season, molded fat baits are being widely scattered throughout known fox areas. These baits contain chemicals that inhibit reproduction among the foxes although they do it no other harm.

We now know that the population of any species can get out of hand and, according to some biologists and game managers, must be *locally* suppressed.

The World of the Red Fox

How many red foxes are there in North America? No one really knows. Ernest Thompson Seton was one of the few interested enough to try to determine a figure. From his extensive observations and calculations, he estimated that most animals can stand about a 20 per cent reduction in their numbers and still maintain the *status quo*. He thereby reasoned that, if you knew from trapping reports exactly how many foxes were being taken each year and the number did not decrease, you would at least have a minimal base population figure. Seton thought that the population could be a lot higher but could not go lower without a decline in the fur reports.

Today very few game departments have any records on the total number of foxes taken in their respective states each year. The most complete records that I have been able to obtain on the red fox are

The silver fox has long been hunted for its coat.

those from North Dakota. However, these figures fluctuate so widely, as a result of the plummeting price of red fox pelts, that it is impossible to apply Seton's formula using the 20 per cent figure. The figures from North Dakota were obtained by the state from the eleven large fur companies that purchased the bulk of the furs taken in that state. It must be remembered that some additional furs had probably been sold to other small fur dealers or other out-of-state companies and thus had not been recorded. No bounty on foxes is paid in North Dakota at the present time; the bounty was discontinued after 1961.

Red Fox Records from North Dakota

Trapping year	Number of red foxes bountied	Number of red fox pelts sold	Average price paid per red fox pelt	Total value of red fox fur harvest
1937-38	*	2,805	$4.32	$ 12,122
1938-39	*	4,882	4.80	23,459
1939-40	*	4,193	5.85	24,584
1940-41	*	7,611	6.72	51,207
1941-42	*	7,927	8.15	64,761
1942-43	*	7,935	8.00	63,480
1943-44	*	20,382	12.76	258,767
1944-45	*	7,657	6.63	50,754
1945-46	*	16,084	5.19	83,475
1946-47	*	8,351	2.68	22,380
1947-48	*	8,750	1.77	15,487
1948-49	*	3,747	.82	3,087
1949-50	*	3,922	.80	3,137
1950-51	*	7,612	1.22	9,279
1951-52	*	3,696	.47	1,720
1952-53	*	1,804	.48	860
1953-54	20,014	1,774	.30	522
1954-55	29,251	2,129	.38	809
1955-56	34,596	2,667	.31	902
1956-57	17,678	349	.26	90
1957-58	20,495	935	.34	316
1958-59	38,000	2,701	.31	837
1959-60	48,016	35,262	1.77	62,414

*No records were available to me, but as the fur prices were high from 1937 to 1947 this would be near the total number of foxes taken.

In 1922 Seton estimated that Pennsylvania had one red fox to every 2.25 square miles of area, based on the fact that 3,525 red foxes were bountied. His estimate for a state total was 20,000 red foxes. In talking with the Pennsylvania Game Commission Bounty Department, I was given the following figures for the past ten years on bountied red foxes:

1956-57	17,849
1957-58	18,125
1958-59	17,667
1959-60	16,087
1960-61	15,502
1961-62	18,406
1962-63	14,089
1963-64	16,318
1964-65	17,101
1965-66	16,816

Totaling these figures shows that 167,960 red foxes were bountied in ten years for an average of 16,796 foxes per year. Using Seton's formula of 20 per cent, which can be done because the bounty number was holding steady, we find that Pennsylvania is supporting about 83,980 red foxes. That is more than four times the red fox population figure of Seton's time. That even this large population of red foxes is not considered detrimental to wildlife or to the sportsman's interest can be seen from the fact that Pennsylvania has now removed the bounty on the red fox.

In 1922 Seton estimated that the red fox had a range of about 5,000,000 square miles in North America and figured conservatively that this area had a total red fox population of about 750,000. We know that the red fox has greatly expanded both its range and its numbers since 1922, so I do not think we would be remiss in saying that the red fox population in North America today is between three and four million.

As this is being written in March, 1968, the price of red fox pelts has again started to rise, and a good one brings about $4.50. This is a far cry from the $35 apiece that was paid for red fox pelts in 1919, but it is a much better price than the forty to fifty cents paid in 1952 and 1953.

Although the prices are slowly creeping up, it is unlikely that they will ever return to the 1919 prices. The fox population can produce more than the demand. It is also unlikely that fox farming will ever again be as profitable as it formerly was. From the 1890's to 1945, the fox farm business had a meteoric rise and fall.

Charles Dalton and Robert Oulton on Prince Edward Island, Canada, became the first to raise silver and black foxes commercially. They sold one black fox pelt on the Paris fur market in 1889 for $2,625. In 1900, they sold three silver fox pelts on the London fur market for a total of $5,103. Between times, they sold breeding stock at $35,000 a pair. Hans Ervetson, of Norway, produced a platinum mutation fox, and one of its offspring brought the highest price ever paid for a fox pelt when it was sold in New York for $11,000.

Such high prices created a tremendous growth of fox farms, which sprang up almost everywhere. One of the largest, the Fromm Fur Farm in Hamburg, Wisconsin, covered 13,100 acres and employed 400 people, including full-time veterinarians to check on the foxes' health. The foxes consumed 10,000 head of cattle and horses, 1,000 tons of bread, 1,000 tons of cereal, 600,000 pounds of liver, 800,000 pounds of carrots, 100 tons of lettuce, additional canned and fresh vegetables, and a carload of cod liver oil annually. At its peak, the farm produced 12,000 silver foxes a year, and before they went out of business they had produced $18,000,000 worth of fur.

The depression, the glut on the fox fur market, and the change in women's tastes and fashions caused such a decline in prices that most fur farms had to close.

Today the fox is gaining its rightful place as a game animal. The red fox does not control any of its prey species. It can only be considered a control on imported or expanding wildlife; with native species it shares in the annual increases or surpluses. The predator does naturally what all human wildlife and stock breeders try to do: it gets rid of inferior stock. Nature's law, "survival of the fittest," has produced the beautiful wild creatures that we know today, and among the most beautiful is the red fox. The aesthetic value to the average person who gets a glimpse of a red fox daintily going about its foxy business is beyond calculation. The red fox is neither good nor bad; it is merely a red fox, admirably fulfilling the niche for which it was created.

Appendix

THE FOLLOWING abbreviated notes are just as I wrote them in the journal that I kept on my trip to Mount McKinley, Alaska, in June of 1966. They contain some of the most continuous and complete notes ever taken on one fox family. Because it does not really get dark at night in the summer in Alaska, we were able to work around the clock and often did. Charlie and Ruth Travers are experts on wolves, and that summer they followed the wolves' activities all night long. It was natural that we should team up. I let them know of wolf activity that I saw in the daytime, and they informed me of any fox activity at the den I was watching.

Friday, June 24, 1966. Awake at 5 A.M. Read and wrote until 6:30 A.M. Had sourdough pancakes for breakfast. It was raining but had started to break at 8:00 A.M. We, Mike Smith, my son Lenny IV and I, drove out to Highway Pass to look for golden plovers. A big gray wolf stood about 100 feet off the road. We all piled out and got some photos. We located the plover's nest but it got so cloudy that we decided to wait till it cleared. We were sitting in the truck camper talking with Mal Lockwood when Dr. Adolph Murie came by. He had spotted a red fox digging out a ground squirrel a short distance up the road. We all went out and took some pictures although we could not approach any closer than about 75 feet. Although the job was futile, the fox was persistent and kept at it for about three hours. Dr. Murie stated that he

167

A red fox tries to unearth a ground squirrel. Adolph Murie had never seen a fox expend so much energy in trying to dig out one of these animals.

had never seen a red fox concentrate that much time and effort on a ground squirrel before. She really made the dirt fly with her front feet. At times the hole was so deep that only her tail was visible. You could see her pull and chew at the roots. She voided once and attempted to cover the droppings with her nose as she does when caching food. Just before noon, the fox trotted off. After we had eaten lunch the fox came back and we took a few more photos before it left for good. At 2:00 P.M., the sun came out and we got the plover pictures. Also some of wild flowers. Then drove to Polychrome Pass where we saw about 2,000 caribou but they were quite a distance away and scattered. Saw a grizzly sow and two cubs. To bed at 10:00 P.M.

Saturday, June 25. Woke up at 3:00 A.M., read and wrote till 5:00 A.M. and then got up. Overcast again—five wolves had tried on three occasions to make a kill on caribou in Toklat Basin and had failed. After breakfast, Mike and Mal went to photo glacier and Lenny and I started for Eielson Mountain for sheep. At Highway Pass we saw a rock ptarmigan and stopped to get pictures. As we did, we saw the same red fox vixen in the same area as yesterday. I could recognize it as the same female that we saw yesterday because she had shed two large patches of her winter hair from her flank area. We promptly called her "Patches." I followed her as she hunted and Lenny worked on the ptarmigan. The female was stalking small birds in a patch of dwarf willows. When stalking she would slink along the ground until her body was no more than six to eight inches high. She caught one vole which she bit in the head, tossed it into the air, caught it in her mouth. She chewed on it a couple of times and swallowed it whole. She had caught the mouse by pouncing on it with her front feet.

She was sleepy and wanted to curl up and sleep but my being in the distance made her reluctant to do so. She followed every little draw and gully which kept her out of sight and out of the constant wind. Because of these gullies I'm willing to bet that ninety per cent of all fox move-

A red fox stalks its prey.

ments and activities are unseen and unsuspected. She finally curled up and put her face on her tail.

I left her, and as I walked towards Lenny, a silver fox came over the ridge and we both took a few pictures. As the ptarmigan had flown, we then walked back towards the fox. At our approach she ran across the flat and up the hill. As we climbed up the hill we discovered a large male red fox sleeping under the bushes. As we neared, he crept back into thicker cover and went to sleep. The female was about 100 yards away and had curled up.

All of a sudden she let out a squalling, yowling yap and went tearing up the hill at full speed. When she got there the male was barking and advanced to her. She dropped flat on her stomach with muzzle outstretched on the ground, tail pluming high in the air, jerking about constantly. The male came over and they touched muzzles, he then smelled her vagina. They both kept the noise up for about ten minutes. It was a real expression of happiness. Then they separated and hunted around. I thought there might be a den in the side hill but it was too wet to look. The female finally disappeared over the hill and the male dropped down to the gravel bar and curled up. He barked once or twice and the female came running back from out of sight. Their hearing is terrific. Then both foxes crossed the snow bank and followed down the gravel bar for a quarter of a mile. The male curled up and slept and I stayed with him while Len followed the female.

Suddenly some caribou ran by, chased by a big, black wolf. When the female fox saw the wolf, it took out as if it was shot and ran at full speed up the south hill about one mile away. The male was alert to all the sounds even though it was 300 yards away. Even while he slept, his ears twitched constantly. He didn't appear to use his eyes or his nose but he sure relied on the ears. We took a lot of pictures, some as close as eight feet. All of a sudden a ground squirrel ran by about 25 feet back up on the bank. The fox shot out of the draw as if it were cata-

A red fox dozes in the sun.

The fox is suddenly awake and watchful. Foxes seldom go into a deep sleep unless they are safe from danger.

pulted. It didn't catch the squirrel but sniffed around the several burrows and made a few desultory attempts to dig it out.

Then the male trotted up the gravel bar and then loped off over one of the north hills.

Lenny and I then worked on caribou and grizzly bear for the balance of the day.

Sunday, June 26. Rained all day. Temperature down to 42° F. Snow is covering the peaks. We didn't take a single photo all day. Thankful for the furnace in the camper. Wrote columns and articles all day.

Monday, June 27. Awoke at 2:45 A.M. Wrote till 5:00 A.M. and then got up and we had breakfast. It is clear out and the snow on the mountain peaks looks like powdered sugar. Very pretty. Took a few red squirrel pictures around the campsite and then went to find a willow ptarmigan's nest that the road crew had discovered. Rain shower delayed us but it cleared again and we got the needed pictures.

Drove out to Highway Pass and had lunch, then carefully searched the area until we found the foxes' den. The male was there and could be recognized by the heavy fur around his neck. We called him "Ruff." Took pictures with the telephoto lens. Some of the pups came out of the burrow. They are dark brown, have blue eyes and are very skittish. I judged them to be about six weeks old. The female came in carrying a vole which she cached nearby. The area is full of caches. I could easily find the caches because the sphagnum moss that was used as a plug to cover the hole would dry and turn brown in contrast with the green undisturbed moss. I opened the cache and photoed the vole. Male came back and we took pictures of it and pups. The fox calls the pups out of the den with a whining MMMMM sound, uttered very low.

When the male left, I followed him for about two hours and five miles. When a fox trots, it is faster than a man can walk. When he lopes, you have to run and still can't keep up. Saw the male dash up over the bank of a gully and catch a ground squirrel. He bit it in the head and then carried it off and cached it in a gravel bank. He covered it with his nose. Then he got so far ahead of me that I lost him and had to return to the camper.

I set up a camouflage blind near the den and sat for three hours but had no luck. After supper it rained and then cleared.

About 8:20 P.M. the female came in carrying a ground squirrel. I tried for photos but had no luck. The female went down into the den for about ten minutes. When she came out she did not loiter but went out hunting. Back to the camper and to bed at 10:00 P.M.

Tuesday, June 28. A crystal clear day until 3:00 P.M., then it clouded up. Up at 3:00 A.M., had breakfast and was at the den and in the blind by 3:30 A.M. At 3:54 A.M., the female came in carrying a vole which she fed to the pups. One pup took the vole underground while the other pups nursed for six minutes. The vixen usually starts nursing the pups from the sitting position and then stands up. The pups in their eagerness often caused her to lift one of her hind legs off the ground. The pups paw at the mother's stomach while nursing in the standing position, the same as they would do in the "lying on the side" position in which position most animals nurse their young. Occasionally, one of the pups would knock another pup loose from a nipple and there is a lot of commotion until it can locate another one. When the female left, the pups played outside for twelve minutes and then went underground.

4:25 A.M. A vole ran down the pathway and over the fox den and into the willows beyond.

5:30 A.M. A herd of thirty caribou bulls came up the valley and split on either side of the blind and passed on.

6:00 A.M. The female came in carrying an arctic ground squirrel which she cached about forty feet from the den. She did not call the pups out and soon left.

175

A red fox nurses her pups.

6:28 A.M. I could hear the pups barking from the den although they did not come out.

7:57 A.M. The male came in carrying a very bloody arctic ground squirrel. He called the pups out and two of the pups had a tug of war with the squirrel and then they both pulled the squirrel underground to feed on it. The male then left.

8:30 A.M. The female came in carrying an arctic ground squirrel. She circled the den going to all the entrances calling the pups. One pup took the squirrel underground. The other two pups tried to nurse. The female is evidently weaning the pups because she only allows them to nurse for a short period of time and then lies down on her belly, covering her nipples. The pups take this as an excuse to play and they climb all over her. The mother is very affectionate and frequently caresses the pups with her tongue. When the pups devil her too much, she gets up and moves off a short distance and then lies down again. She stayed at the den till 9:03 A.M., then got up and walked within a few feet of my blind as she left. The pups played a few minutes and then went underground.

For the next eight hours there was no fox activity at all although I could watch caribou activity from the blind.

5:33 P.M. The male came in carrying one and a half ground squirrels. He trotted right up to the main entrance, dropped the squirrels and called out the pups. From the very start, the male was much more tolerant of my presence than was the female.

5:38 P.M. The female came in with a large arctic ground squirrel. When she saw the male, she dropped the squirrel and bounded towards the male, whining and yowling as before. She went through the same crouching, tail wagging and nuzzling performance that I had witnessed before. The male reciprocated and then left when a car stopped on the road above the den. The female cached the squirrel and then left.

9:15 P.M. The female came in. Evidently she had been unsuccessful

A red fox brings a ground squirrel to her pups.

in her hunting because she dug up the cached squirrel, chewed off the head and then fed the balance to the pups. One pup fed on the squirrel and the other two nursed for about ten minutes. The female stayed around for another ten minutes and left. The pups stayed outside and played for sixteen to seventeen minutes. This is the longest period of time that I have seen them stay out of the den without the parents around. This time will gradually increase as they get older.

10:00 P.M. I left the blind after 10:00 when Charlie Travers came to watch wolves. There was no fox activity until 3:00 A.M. the next day.

Wednesday, June 29. Up at 3:00 A.M. and at the den at 3:12 A.M. Ruth Travers and I watched the female come in to feed a ground squirrel to the pups. Then she left. Ruth and Charlie copied my notes for their records and then they left.

5:15 A.M. The female came in, dropped a couple of voles and nursed the pups. She was around the den for about 28 minutes and left.

I sat at the den all day until a tremendous storm drove me out just before 4:00 P.M. There had been no fox activity all day.

5:30 P.M. We drove past the den going back to the park head-quarters for gasoline and supplies. The female was lying at the main entrance which means that she probably had come in right after the storm.

Thursday, June 30. These observations are from Charlie Travers's notes.

3:27 A.M. Female came in with a ground squirrel. The squirrel had either been caught early or had been cached because its body was stiff. Two pups met her at the den entrance and pulled the squirrel underground. No nursing took place. She looked around for a minute and left at 3:39 A.M.

6:35 A.M. Female came in with three voles. Each pup took a vole and went underground with them. One pup came right back out and nursed. Then the other two nursed but only two or three minutes each. Female then walked off into the willows and lay down. She washed one pup as it climbed over her. She left at 6:45 A.M. and the pup joined the rest in the burrow.

9:25 A.M. Female came in with a vole but pups were more interested in playing. She did not allow any pup to nurse although one tried. Evidently the pups annoyed her because she got up and lay down in three different places, finally leaving at 9:55 A.M.

4:00 P.M. I was back at the den but no activity until 9:00 P.M.

9:00 P.M. Female came in with no food and allowed the pups to nurse. In about fifteen minutes she left.

9:30 P.M. The female came in with a vole which she gave to one pup and then she left.

The next notes are from Charlie and Ruth Travers.

10:38 P.M. The male appeared south of the den running very hard towards it. He came right across the main den and dropped the voles he was carrying and went right beyond the den to the east and sat down watching a young bull moose intently. Female arrived at the same time from the west. She went to the main entrance and allowed pups to nurse for about three minutes. Then she gathered up the voles dropped by the male and fed them to the pups.

10:45 P.M. Ruth tried to work closer to the den very cautiously in order to see better. Hearing cars coming, she sank down out of sight to avoid attracting attention to the den. When the vixen saw this sinking action as though it were an animal stalking, she gave a warning noise and the pups piled into the den and stayed there. Then the vixen advanced to within fifteen feet looking at Ruth very closely and barked. She reacted to Ruth just as she had done with a porcupine.

11:30 P.M. The male came past our camper. I was sitting in the cab writing and saw him drop a vole, a small bird and something else that I couldn't see clearly. He then bounded around in the bushes as if hunting for a vole. He had no success and came back, picked up his prey and went on up toward the den.

Friday, July 1. Up at 2:20 A.M. and at the den at 2:30 A.M. Crystal clear, cold and very windy.

8:35 A.M. Although I had seen caribou, no fox activity until now when the female came in with a fresh ground squirrel. She allowed the pups to nurse several times and lay down in several different spots. She left at 9:05 A.M.

9:45 A.M. Female came in and left almost at once. Had a ground squirrel.

2:30 P.M. Lenny took some photos of the female fox at the den. Sky clouding up and a hard rain made us quit.

Saturday, July 2. From Charlie Travers's notes.

2:38 A.M. Female arrived with three voles. She called to pups while she was still twenty to thirty feet from den. The pups met her at the den's entrance and began to nurse while she was in sitting position. They nursed about six minutes. Then female went back, gathered up the voles and gave them to the pups, meanwhile making a mewing, cat-like sound. Pups ate the voles outside the den and this is the first time that that has occurred. One pup lost its vole under its mother's tail. It then began to play with the tail instead of eating, but it had already nursed for six minutes so probably wasn't hungry. Female left den at 2:53 A.M. and pups stayed out till 2:58 A.M., then went underground.

3:30 A.M. I came to the den at this time but got no photos till 8:28 A.M. when female came in with two voles which she fed to pups. Two pups nursed while female stood. I never saw her nurse the pups lying down but I feel that the female prefers to sit or stand so that she can constantly look over the tops of the dwarf willows.

8:35 A.M. A car stopped on the road and three people came down towards the den and the female left at once. As there is practically no activity at the den between 9 A.M. and 5 P.M., I decided to follow the female all day, if possible.

I followed the fox to the road and watched her make a stalk and a pounce but she missed as I saw a bird fly up and away. She started up the road again and stopped to make another stalk. A car stopped and a man jumped out and began taking movies. The fox ignored him and continued stalking. The driver got out and threw rocks at the fox so the other man could get action on his movie camera. I threatened them with a rock and after exchanging unpleasantries, I followed the fox away from the road. She made another stalk through a swale and missed. Long-tailed Jaegers often dived at the fox while it was hunting, and now one flew down and hit the fox in the head five times. She then went up to the top of Stoney Dome where she caught a vole. Returned to den at 8:53 A.M. and fed third pup. She walked around and lay down four times and snapped at pups that tried to nurse. She kept searching the horizon as if looking for the male.

9:45 A.M. She left the den after spending the longest period there yet. She went down to the culvert and then left the road to dig up a large vole cached there. She carried the vole across the road and recached it. Then she started towards Stoney Creek. She made two four-footed jumps and caught another vole. She had caught two voles in ten minutes and headed right back to den where she arrived at 9:56 A.M. and fed the pups.

10:00 A.M. Female left the den and hunted the south base of Stoney Dome, then up to the top and then back down again, continued along base.

10:19 A.M. Female curled up beneath some willows and went to sleep.

1:07 P.M. Sun shining on the female woke her up and she moved about fifty feet up the hillside and got in the shade of a high hummock. As I write this, I am lying just eight feet away from her. Like a person, the fox moved around quite a bit while she slept.

182

3:01 P.M. A bird noise awoke the fox and she stalked up to the top of Stoney Dome but had no luck. At the top she again curled into a ball and slept at 3:06 P.M.

4:01 P.M. The female got up and hunted north along the ridge, then curled up again.

4:17 P.M. She woke up with a start and ran at full speed to the edge of the rim where she stopped and peered intently over the rim. Finally, she dashed down the spine at full speed. She bounced around from side to side searching for the ground squirrel which had awakened her but had no luck. The area was full of ground squirrel burrows. Then she slid down the talus slope, I slid down the talus slope, she crossed Stoney Creek on the rocks, I crossed Stoney Creek on the rocks, she loped up the opposite mountain but I didn't. I can't keep up with her when she lopes on the level and I sure can't keep up going up a hill. I'm only a mere mortal and maybe more mere than most. Not wanting to lose track of her, I hurried up as fast as I could till my heart hurt and my lungs ached. I found her on top and got a few pictures as she crossed a snowfield. Then I lost and found her again.

4:37 P.M. The female lay down and slept for ten minutes and was I ever thankful for the break. When she got up at 4:47 P.M., she rolled on her back, stretched and squirmed, just as my springer spaniels do. I had trouble with my camera and did not get any photos of this action. I then headed back to the camper about an hour's walk away.

Sunday, July 3. Got to the den at 8:05 A.M.

9:42 A.M. The female came in with one vole. She cached the vole and nursed the pups for about three minutes. She stayed around for 27 minutes, walking about, lying down and playing with the pups.

10:10 A.M. Female left den because too many cars on the road made her nervous. She went down through the culvert. She hunted up and down the slopes of the dry wash. Dug up a cached caribou calf leg, probably scavenged from a wolf kill, ate some meat, drank some water, voided and then continued north up the wash.

183

A red fox listens intently to a vole beneath the grass.

The fox tries to dig out the vole.

10:40 A.M. She lay down in some willows just ten feet from ground squirrel that was standing erect watching her. The fox did not see the squirrel and went to sleep.

11:12 A.M. The squirrel finally moved and chirped and the fox came out of its sleep like a released coiled spring but missed the squirrel. She then trotted down the wash and went up a draw. She crawled under some undercut snow banks for several minutes then came up on the bank and lay down in a thicket at 11:24 A.M.

11:43 A.M. A robin discovered the sleeping fox and sat in a bush up over the fox and kept uttering its single, piercing alarm note, all the while flicking its wings and wagging its tail. A redpoll soon joined in the commotion and then they quit when the fox did not move.

5:10 P.M. Female got up, hunted up a gully leading to North Mountain. Started to stalk a ground squirrel and then quit.

5:17 P.M. She curled up and went to sleep again. The sky has now become very black and I left her at 6:20 P.M. still sleeping.

7:15 P.M. After supper Lenny and I checked out another fox den and saw the female.

Monday, July 4. Up at 3:00 A.M. Went right to the new den. The male fox barked a raspy, squalling bark at me and ran off. Lenny stayed at that den and I went to the den I had been working on.

7:15 A.M. The female came in but had no food and walked right on by. I sketched the den. No activity and at noon I went back to pick up Lenny who had taken some photos of the female at the new den. It started to rain so Mike, Len and I headed back to the park headquarters where we got supplies and left on July 5th.

The following notes were sent to me by Charlie Travers after I had left the park:

Monday, July 4. 5:58 A.M. Female returned with three voles which she dropped near the main entrance. She put her head into main

A red fox yawns, preparatory to taking a snooze.

entrance while standing on the mound and called with a low grunt. The pups responded immediately to her grunting and began to nurse as soon as they could become attached. Female standing. Nursing for complete three minutes in standing position. Female then lay down and a single pup climbed up on her and over her head to chew on her muzzle.

6:13 A.M. Female left den heading northwest, passing through the culvert as she proceeded.

6:15 A.M. Terminated observations.

Tuesday, July 5. 6:17 A.M. Female returned to den after I had been in position only two minutes. Nursed pups for only two minutes, then interested them in the four voles she had brought with her. Female played with pups, but was apparently on lookout for the male as she frequently stood up to see out over vegetation. Left den at 6:35 A.M., minutes after female had departed for morning hunt towards Highway Pass.

6:12 P.M. Back at den—female nursed three minutes, then moved off through culvert to hunt (I thought). I followed her west one and a quarter miles to where she lay down in a patch of willows and curled up until I departed at 7:32 P.M.

Wednesday, July 7. 7:05 A.M. Female again arriving at den with ground squirrel and several voles. Called to young from about ten feet from entrance and then dropped her load. Encouraged pups with soft mewing to take animals which they proceeded to do. Pups carried them into the den, then quickly returned to start nursing. Two pups especially interested in nursing—the other acted more interested in the surroundings, and playing. Vixen left at 7:32 A.M. and I was late to work as I had to drive back to Wonder Lake. No male in view or reported by other photographers during this period.

Thursday, July 8. 3:00 P.M. Female observed moving pups from den site to new location. New den location discovered this day—only 300 yards northwest along the same dry stream bed, on a south-facing slope on very steep ground.

Saturday, July 10. 11:00 A.M. Female observed playfully entertaining her litter at her new home between 9:05 and 10:10 A.M. No observed nursing so assume nursing done early in day.

1:00 P.M. While on road patrol noticed female lying at top of den site, pups then came out to play about den location, and one fellow forced his mother to rise so he could nurse one minute.

Bibliography

Ables, Ernest D. "An Exceptional Fox Movement," *Journal of Mammalogy*, vol. 46, no. 1, p. 102.

Aesop's Fables. Mount Vernon, N. Y.: Peter Pauper Press, 1941.

Allen, John M., ed. "Indiana Pittman-Robertson Wildlife Restoration 1939-1955." Indianapolis, Ind.: Division of Fish and Game, 1957.

Anthony, Harold E. *Field Book of North American Mammals.* New York: G. P. Putnam's Sons, 1928.

Arnold, David A. *Red Foxes of Michigan.* Lansing, Mich.: Michigan Department of Conservation, 1956.

Asdell, S. A. *Patterns of Mammalian Reproduction.* Ithaca, N. Y.: Comstock Publishing Co., Inc., 1946.

Bee, James W., and E. Raymond Hall. *Mammals of Northern Alaska.* Lawrence, Kan.: University of Kansas, 1956.

Berrill, N. J. *Sex and the Nature of Things.* New York: Dodd, Mead & Co., 1953.

Bible, The.

Bourlière, François. *The Natural History of Mammals.* New York: Alfred A. Knopf, Inc., 1954.

Brooks, David M. "Fur Animals of Indiana." Pittman-Robertson Bulletin 4, Indianapolis, Ind.: Indiana Department of Conservation, 1959.

Bump, Gardiner, Robert W. Darrow, Frank C. Edminster, and Walter F. Crissey. *The Ruffed Grouse.* Albany, N. Y.: New York State Conservation Department, 1947.

191

Burns, Eugene. *The Sex Life of Wild Animals.* New York: Rinehart and Co., Inc., 1953.

Burton, Maurice. *Systematic Dictionary of Mammals of the World.* New York: Thomas Y. Crowell Co., 1962.

Cahalane, Victor H. *Mammals of North America.* New York: Macmillan Co., 1947.

Camp, Raymond R., ed. *The Hunter's Encyclopedia.* Harrisburg, Pa.: Stackpole and Heck, Inc., 1948.

Carlson, C. Edward. "A Red Fox Fatality by Self-Entrapment," *Journal of Mammalogy*, vol. 45, no. 2, pp. 318-19.

Churcher, Charles S. "Cranial Variations in the North American Red Fox," *Journal of Mammalogy*, vol. 41, no. 3, 1960.

Cook, David B., and W. J. Hamilton, Jr. "The Ecological Relationships of Red Fox Food in Eastern New York," *Ecology*, vol. 25, pp. 91-104.

Crandall, Lee S. *The Management of Wild Mammals in Captivity.* Chicago: University of Chicago Press, 1964.

Cronan, John M., and Albert Brooks. "The Mammals of Rhode Island." Wildlife Pamphlet 6. Providence, R. I.: Rhode Island Division of Fish and Game, 1962.

Cross, E. C. "Colour Phases of the Red Fox," *Journal of Mammalogy*, vol. 22, no. 1, pp. 25-39.

Dahlberg, Burton L., and Ralph C. Guettinger. "The White-Tailed Deer in Wisconsin." Technical Wildlife Bulletin 14. Madison, Wis.: Wisconsin Conservation Department, 1956.

Devoe, Alan. *This Fascinating Animal World.* New York: McGraw-Hill Book Co., Inc., 1951.

Dixon, Joseph S. "Birds and Mammals of Mt. McKinley National Park, Alaska." Fauna Series 3. Washington, D.C.: U.S. Government Printing Office, 1938.

Dodds, Donald G. "Food Habits of the Newfoundland Red Fox," *Journal of Mammalogy*, vol. 36, no. 2, p. 291.

Bibliography

Douglass, Donald W., and G. W. Bradt. *The Red Fox—Friend or Foe.* Lansing, Mich.: Game Division, Michigan Department of Conservation, 1945.

Dout, J. Kenneth, Caroline A. Heppenstall, and John E. Guilday. *Mammals of Pennsylvania.* Harrisburg, Pa.: Pennsylvania Game Commission, 1966.

Dufresne, Frank. *Alaska's Animals and Fishes.* Portland, Ore.: Binfords and Mort, 1946.

Elton, Charles. *Voles, Mice, Lemmings.* Weinheim, Germany: J. Cramer, 1965.

Errington, Paul. "Food Habits of Iowa Red Foxes During a Drought Summer," *Ecology,* vol. 18, pp. 53-61.

————. "Food Habits of Mid-West Foxes," *Journal of Mammalogy,* vol. 16, no. 3, pp. 192-200.

————. *Of Predation and Life.* Ames, Iowa: Iowa State University Press, 1967.

Fichter, Edson, and Roger Williams. "Distribution and Status of the Red Fox in Idaho," *Journal of Mammalogy,* vol. 48, no. 2, pp. 219-30.

Fisher, Harvey I. "Notes on the Red Fox in Missouri," *Journal of Mammalogy,* vol. 32, no. 3, pp. 296-99.

Furbearers No. 1. "The Fox in New Hampshire." Technical Circular, Concord, N. H.

Gray, James. *How Animals Move.* London: Cambridge University Press, 1953.

Hall, E. Raymond, and Keith R. Kelson, *The Mammals of North America.* New York: The Ronald Press Co., 1959.

Hamilton, W. J., Jr. *American Mammals.* New York: McGraw-Hill Book Co., Inc., 1939.

————. "Notes on Food of Red Foxes in New York and New England," *Journal of Mammalogy,* vol. 16, no. 1, pp. 16-21.

Harper, Francis. *Land and Fresh Water Mammals of the Ungava*

193

Peninsula. Lawrence, Kan.: University of Kansas Press, 1961.

Heit, William S. "Food Habits of Red Foxes of the Maryland Marshes," *Journal of Mammalogy,* vol. 25, no. 1, pp. 55-58.

Henderson, Junius, and Elberta Craig, *Economic Mammalogy.* Baltimore, Md.: Charles C. Thomas, 1932.

Hibbard, Edmund A. "A Badger-Fox Episode," *Journal of Mammalogy,* vol. 44, no. 2, p. 265.

Higginson, A. Henry. "The Red Fox of America." *The Chronicle of the Horse.* Middleburg, Virginia.

Hildebrand, Milton. *Comparative Morphology of the Body Skeleton in Recent Canidae.* Berkeley, Calif.: University of California Press, 1954.

Hingston, R. W. G. *The Meaning of Animal Colour and Adornment.* London: Edward Arnold and Co., 1933.

Hoffman, Roger A., and Charles M. Kirkpatrick. "Red Fox Weights and Reproduction in Tippecanoe County, Indiana," *Journal of Mammalogy,* vol. 35, no. 4, pp. 504-9.

Hoffmeister, Donald F., and Carol O. Mohr. "Fieldbook of Illinois Mammals." Manual 4, Illinois Natural History Survey. Urbana, Ill.: 1957.

Holcomb, Larry C. "Large Litter of Red Fox," *Journal of Mammalogy,* vol. 46, no. 3, p. 530.

Hornaday, W. T. *American Natural History.* New York: Charles Scribner's Sons, 1935.

Jackson, Hartley H. T. *Mammals of Wisconsin.* Madison, Wis.: University of Wisconsin Press, 1961.

Kagan, Irving G., Lois Norman, and Paul D. Leiby. "Biologic Identification of the Cestode *Echinococcus Multilocularis* Isolated From Foxes in North Dakota," *The Journal of Parasitology,* vol. 51, no. 5, October 1965, pp. 807-8.

Kalm, Peter. *Travels in North America (1770).* New York: Dover Publications, Inc., 1966.

Bibliography

Keith, Lloyd B. *Wildlife's Ten-Year Cycle*. Madison, Wis.: University of Wisconsin Press, 1963.

Kolb, Helen, supervisor. *High School Biology—Green Version*. Chicago: Rand McNally and Co., 1963.

Korschgen, Leroy J. "Food Habits of the Red Fox in Missouri," *Journal of Mammalogy*, vol. 23, no. 2, pp. 168-76.

Lapage, Geoffrey. *Animals Parasitic in Man*. New York: Dover Publications, Inc., 1963.

Latham, Roger M. *The Ecology and Economics of Predator Management*. Harrisburg, Pa.: Pennsylvania Game Commission, 1951.

————. *An Ecological Study of the Red and Gray Foxes in Southeastern Pennsylvania*. Harrisburg, Pa.: Pennsylvania Game Commission, 1943.

Linhart, Samuel B. "Rabies in Wildlife and Control Methods in New York State," *New York Fish and Game Journal*, vol. 7, no. 1, 1960.

Longley, William H. "Movements of Red Fox," *Journal of Mammalogy*, vol. 43, no. 1, p. 107.

MacPherson, A. H. "A Northward Range Extension of the Red Fox in the Eastern Canadian Arctic," *Journal of Mammalogy*, vol. 45, no. 1, pp. 138-40.

McSpadden, J. Walker, ed. *Animals of the World*. Garden City, N. Y.: Garden City Publishing Co., 1942.

Mansueti, Romeo. "Extinct and Vanishing Mammals of Maryland and District of Columbia," *Maryland Naturalist*, Winter-Spring Issue, 1950.

Martin, A. C. et al. *American Wildlife and Plants*. New York: McGraw-Hill Book Co., Inc., 1951.

Merriam, H. Gray. "An Unusual Fox-Woodchuck Relationship," *Journal of Mammalogy*, vol. 44, no. 1, pp. 115-16.

Miller, Gerrit S., Jr., and Remington Kellogg. "List of North American Recent Mammals." United States National Museum Bulletin 205. Washington, D.C.: Smithsonian Institute, 1955.

Milne, Lorus J. and Margery. *The Senses of Animals and Men.* New York: Atheneum, 1962.

Mitchell, Kenneth A. *The Status of the Red Fox in West-Central Ohio.* Columbus, Ohio: Ohio Wildlife Research Station, Ohio State University, 1941.

Moore, Clifford B. *Ways of Mammals, in Fact and Fancy.* New York: The Ronald Press Co., 1953.

Murie, Adolph. *Following Fox Trails.* Ann Arbor, Mich.: University of Michigan Press, 1936.

———. *Mammals of Mt. McKinley National Park, Alaska.* Alaska: Mt. McKinley Natural History Association, Mt. McKinley National Park, 1962.

Murie, Olaus J. *Fauna of the Aleutian Islands and Alaska Peninsula.* Washington, D.C.: United States Department of the Interior, Fish and Wildlife Service, 1959.

———. *A Field Guide to Animal Tracks.* Boston: Houghton Mifflin Co., 1954.

Ognev, S. I. *Mammals of Eastern Europe and Northern Asia.* Trans. from Russian for the National Science Foundation. Washington, D.C.: 1962.

Paradiso, John L. *Mammals of Maryland.* Unpublished at this time.

Parker, Richard, James Kelly, E. L. Cheatum, and Donald J. Dean. "Fox Population Densities in Relation to Rabies," *New York Fish and Game Journal,* vol. 4, 1957.

Peattie, Donald Culross. *Sportsman's Country.* Boston: Houghton Mifflin Co., 1952.

Peterson, Randolph L. *The Mammals of Eastern Canada.* Toronto: Oxford University Press, 1966.

Pryor, Lorenzo B. "Sarcoptic Mange in Wild Foxes in Pennsylvania," *Journal of Mammalogy,* vol. 37, no. 1, pp. 90-93.

Richards, Stephen H., and Ruth L. Hine. "Wisconsin Fox Populations." Technical Bulletin 6. Madison, Wis.: Wisconsin Conservation Department, 1953.

Rue, Leonard Lee III. *Cottontail.* New York: Thomas Y. Crowell Co.,
1965.

————. *The World of the White-tailed Deer.* Philadelphia and New
York: J. B. Lippincott Co., 1962.

Rutter, Russell J., and Douglas H. Pimlott, *The World of the Wolf.*
Philadelphia and New York: J. B. Lippincott Co., 1968.

Schofield, Raymond D. "Litter Size and Age Ratios of Michigan Red
Foxes," *Journal of Wildlife Management,* vol. 22, no. 3, pp.
313-15.

————. "A Thousand Miles of Fox Trails in Michigan's Ruffed
Grouse Range," *Journal of Wildlife Management,* vol. 24, no. 4,
pp. 432-34.

Schoonmaker, W. J., *The World of the Woodchuck.* Philadelphia and
New York: J. B. Lippincott Co., 1966.

Schueler, Robert L. "Red Fox Food Habits in a Wilderness Area,"
Journal of Mammalogy, vol. 32, no. 4, pp. 462-64.

Schwartz, Charles W. and Elizabeth R. *The Wild Mammals of Missouri.* Kansas City, Mo.: University of Missouri Press and Missouri Conservation Commission, 1959.

Scott, Thomas G. "Comparative Analysis of Red Fox Feeding Trends
on Two Central Iowa Areas." Research Bulletin 353. Ames, Iowa:
Iowa State Agricultural Experiment Station, 1947.

————. "An Evaluation of the Red Fox." Biological Notes, no. 35.
Urbana, Ill.: Illinois Natural History Survey, 1955.

————. "Some Food Coactions of the Northern Plains Red Fox."
Journal Paper J-1131. Ames, Iowa: Iowa Agricultural Experiment
Station, 1943.

Scott, Thomas G., and Willard D. Klimstra. *Red Foxes and a Declining Prey Population.* Illinois Natural History Survey, Carbondale,
Ill.: University of Southern Illinois Press, 1955.

Scott, William B. *A History of Land Mammals in the Western Hemi-*

sphere. New York: Hafner Publishing Co., 1962.

Seagers, Clayton B. *The Fox in New York*. Albany, N. Y.: New York State Conservation Department, 1944.

Seton, Ernest Thompson. *Lives of Game Animals*. Boston: Charles T. Branford Co., 1953.

Sheldon, William G. "Denning Habits and Home Range of Red Foxes in New York State," *Journal of Wildlife Management*, vol. 14, no. 1, 1950, pp. 33-42.

————. "Reproductive Behavior of Foxes in New York State," *Journal of Mammalogy*, vol. 30, no. 3, pp. 236-46.

Shillinger, J. E. "Diseases of Fur Animals." Farmer's Bulletin 1777. Washington, D.C.: United States Department of Agriculture, 1937.

Sikes, R. Keith, ed. *Zoonoses Surveillance*. Atlanta, Ga.: National Communicable Disease Center, 1967.

Silver, Helenette. *History of New Hampshire Game and Furbearers*. Concord, N. H.: New Hampshire Fish and Game Department, 1957.

Smith, Lawrence F. "Internal Parasites of the Red Fox in Iowa," *Journal of Wildlife Management*, vol. 7, no. 2, 1943.

State Game and Fish Department. *The Red Fox in North Dakota*. Bismarck, N. Dak.: 1949.

Stefferud, Alfred, ed. "Animal Diseases." *Yearbook 1956*, Washington, D.C.: United States Department of Agriculture.

Storm, Gerald L. "Movements and Activities of Foxes as Determined by Radio Tracking," *Journal of Wildlife Management*, vol. 29, no. 1, pp. 1-13.

————, and Ernest D. Ables. "Notes on Newborn and Full-Term Wild Red Foxes," *Journal of Mammalogy*, vol. 47, no. 1, pp. 116-18.

Sullivan, Edward G., and Arnold O. Haugen. "Age Determination of Foxes by X-Ray of Forefeet," *Journal of Wildlife Management*, vol. 20, no. 2, 1956, pp. 210-12.

Bibliography

Switzenberg, D. F. "Breeding Productivity in Michigan Red Foxes," *Journal of Mammalogy*, vol. 31, no. 2, pp. 194-95.

Trippensee, Reuben Edwin. *Wildlife Management*. New York: McGraw-Hill Book Co., Inc., 1953.

Vincent, Robert E. "Observations of Red Fox Behavior," *Ecology*, vol. 39, no. 4, pp. 755-57.

Walters, Joseph H. "Foxes on Martha's Vineyard, Massachusetts," *Journal of Mammalogy*, vol. 48, no. 1, pp. 137-38.

Waters, Joseph H. "Red Fox and Gray Fox from New England Archeological Sites," *Journal of Mammalogy*, vol. 45, no. 2, 1964.

Webber, C. W. *Wild Scenes and Wild Hunters of the World*. Philadelphia, Pa.: J. W. Bradley, 1852.

Weisz, Paul B. *The Science of Biology*. New York: McGraw-Hill Book Co., Inc., 1959.

Wright, Thomas J. *A Study of the Fox in Rhode Island*. Providence, R. I.: Rhode Island Division of Fish and Game, 1952.

Index